Doctor Robe

The Promis Reco

a new life
healing depression)

PROMIS

The PROMIS Primer

Written by Dr Robert Lefever

PROMIS Recovery Centre Limited
The Old Court House, Pinners Hill
Nonington, Nr. Canterbury
Kent CT15 4LL. UK
www.promis.co.uk

ISBN 1 871013 14 3

Design and production by Rainbow, Ipswich IP5 3RY, England.
Printed in Basauri, Spain by Grafo SA.

**to
all who suffer from
depressive illness or addictive disease
and to our families**

Contents

The Twelve Steps of the Anonymous Fellowships.

We

1. Admitted we were powerless over (our addiction) and that our lives had become unmanageable.

2. Came to believe that a power greater than ourselves could restore us to sanity.

3. Made a decision to turn our will and our lives over to the care of God as we understood Him.

4. Made a searching and fearless moral inventory of ourselves.

5. Admitted to God, to ourselves and to another human being the exact nature of our wrongs.

6. Were entirely ready to have God remove all these defects of character.

7. Humbly asked Him to remove our shortcomings.

8. Made a list of all persons we had harmed and became willing to make amends to them all.

9. Made direct amends to such people wherever possible, except when to do so would injure them or others.

10. Continued to take personal inventory and when we were wrong promptly admitted it.

11. Sought through prayer and meditation to improve our conscious contact with God, as we understood Him, praying only for knowledge of His will for us and the power to carry that out.

12. Having had a spiritual awakening as the result of these Steps, we tried to carry this message to (other addicts) who still suffer and to apply these principles in all our affairs.

The Twelve Steps were first formulated by Alcoholics Anonymous.

The Twelve Promises

Step IX of the Anonymous Fellowships states "Made direct amends to those we had harmed except when to do so would injure them or others". The Big Book of Alcoholics Anonymous (on page 83) in dealing with this ninth step makes the following promises:

"If we are painstaking about this phase of our development, we will be amazed before we are half way through.

1. We are going to know a new freedom and a new happiness.

2. We will not regret the past nor wish to shut the door on it.

3. We will comprehend the word serenity and

4. We will know peace.

5. No matter how far down the scale we have gone, we will see how our experience can benefit others.

6. That feeling of uselessness and self-pity will disappear.

7. We will lose interest in selfish things and gain interest in our fellows.

8. Self-seeking will slip away.

9. Our whole attitude and outlook upon life will change.

10. Fear of people and of economic insecurity will leave us.

11. We will intuitively know how to handle situations which used to baffle us.

12. We will suddenly realise that God is doing for us what we could not do for ourselves."

The Serenity Prayer

God grant me the serenity
To accept the things I cannot change,
Courage to change the things I can
And the wisdom to know the difference.

- Reinhold Niebuhr

Preface

These notes on addictive disease and recovery largely wrote themselves. In addition to my general medical practice and my principal counselling work, I do group therapy and psychodrama sessions each lunchtime and on two evenings on week-days in the PROMIS Counselling Centre in London and at weekends in the PROMIS Recovery Centre in Kent. I ask the patients to choose the subjects for the lectures they wish me to give. They force me to think about the issues most important to them. By speaking spontaneously, and in response to questions or challenges as I go along, I often find myself having to clarify my own thinking. Addicts and their families are not a passive audience!

Sixteen years down the line after helping to treat one hundred and eighty in-patients and three hundred and fifty out-patients each year and having given a total of something close to two thousand lectures, I am still learning from our patients. As I have learnt so much, I thought it might be helpful if I collected the notes into a book. (The notes were written after the lectures, not before.) Even so, I am sure that at the very next lecture I shall learn something new. The subject matter of a new life is infinite.

As an addict myself, and with addicts in my family, I have learned a great deal that has benefited me. I hope that these short notes will return some benefit to others.

The numerical order of the PROMIS lecture notes in this book follows the course of patients' concerns as they progress through treatment. Initially there tends to be intellectual challenge on the nature of addictive disease. Gradually this gives way to questions of personal philosophy. Finally the interest is in maintaining recovery through working the Twelve Step programme in the Anonymous Fellowships.

I am grateful to our patients at PROMIS for their inspiration and stimulus, to my wife Meg for her understanding and patience in running me and the family programme at PROMIS, to our son Robin for his insight and professionalism in managing and running the in-patient and out-patient centres, to our staff for their enthusiasm and support, to my secretary, Sarah Oaten, for her good humour and skill, and to Dr Harriet Harvey-Wood for her exceedingly helpful editorial suggestions.

Dr Robert Lefever. March 2002.

"Hence, loathèd Melancholy,
   Of Cerebrus and blackest Midnight born,
In Stygian cave forlorn,
   'Mongst horrid shapes, and shrieks, and sights unholy!"

John Milton, *L'Allegro*

Depression and Addictive Disease

1. Depression is perhaps the most widely misdiagnosed of all clinical conditions:

    i. Sadness or unhappiness, in response to events, should be termed sadness or unhappiness, rather than given a clinical name that risks being followed by clinical treatment. Sadness and unhappiness are emotional choices according to our personal values: they are the response that we feel is most appropriate in the particular circumstances. As the distinguished psychiatrist, Dr William Glasser, the creator of Reality Therapy and Choice Theory, points out, the word "unhappy" should really be used as a verb: I unhappy, you unhappy, he or she unhappies etc. Unhappiness resolves on its own when our perception of life is modified by time and other events;

    ii. Depressive illness, an imbalance in brain biochemistry, does occur - for example after childbirth - but it is generally exceedingly rare. Mostly the diagnosis "clinical depression" is no more than an excuse to prescribe medication when the doctor has no better ideas (and no better training and experience) on what to do to help the patient. Anti-depressants do have a rare place in the treatment of depressive illness (perhaps better termed "involutional melancholia"), as does electroconvulsive therapy (E.C.T., a generally much over-used and even at times barbaric form of treatment). However, it should be remembered that addicts of one kind or another will often gladly accept anti-depressants and, remarkably, some even accept E.C.T. in order to avoid the diagnosis of addictive disease;

    iii. Addictive disease, probably genetically inherited and mediated through defects of chemical neurotransmission in the mood centres of the brain, is common. It affects probably ten per cent of the population. The diagnosis of depression or clinical depression should never be made until the alternative diagnosis of addictive disease has been fully considered and assessed appropriately. Addicts themselves will always prefer a diagnosis of depression, and a prescription for anti-depressants, rather than facing up to their addictive nature and dealing with it appropriately. If, say, only one in a hundred addicts has a separate depressive illness, each and every one will be convinced that he or she is that one in a hundred;

    iv. Addicts are born rather than made. Our sense of inner emptiness, commonly interpreted as "depression", leads us towards the use of mood-altering substances, processes and relationships in order to help ourselves to feel better. Once discovered, the mood-altering effects are never forgotten. Furthermore, if we abstain we merely revert to the original state of inner emptiness. We then either remain in this "dry-drunk" state, with all the mood disturbances and dysfunctional behaviour even in the absence of its previously discovered "treatments", or we cross-addict into other addictive substances, behaviours and relationships. At this point a diagnosis of "depression" not only takes us further away from the appropriate diagnosis and management of our addictive disease, it risks giving us an additional dependency - a prescription drug addiction.

2. The inner emptiness of addictive disease can be treated appropriately on a day-to-day basis by working the Twelve Step programme of the Anonymous Fellowships. No medications are necessary. The biochemistry of the brain heals itself. Life becomes worthwhile and, with the re-emergence of enthusiasm, we discover the true happiness of achieving our creative potential and making increasingly rewarding relationships.

Addictive Disease

1. Patients don't like being referred to as addicts; they don't mind being diagnosed as being depressed; they are positively delighted to be called stressed. Each term conjures up its own image of strength or weakness, courage or cowardice, responsibility or irresponsibility. Yet these terms are often used simply as social concepts rather than clinical facts and they may get in the way of appropriate diagnosis and treatment.

2. Addictive disease needs to be seen for what it is: a disease of the human spirit, affecting all the beautiful abstracts of life such as hope, love, trust, honour, and innocence.

3. Sigmund Freud battled with his contemporaries over the existence of mental illness as an entity discrete from physical illness. The battle today simply takes this one stage further, separating spiritual disease from mental disease. Addicts have a disease of feeling and perception rather than of thought and will. They need no encouragement to think or control: they do too much of those. Paradoxical though it may appear in the standard light in which addicts are depicted, they need to be helped to give up trying to control their feelings. The prospect of loss of control is what they most fear and it is this fear that keeps them trapped in using one method or another to suppress their feelings.

4 Addictive disease is probably genetically inherited through defects of chemical neurotransmission in the mood centres of the brain. This leads to a susceptibility to the mood-altering properties of various substances, behaviours or relationships. Stressful events give rise to uncomfortable feelings and the sufferer learns how to anaesthetise himself or herself in order to avoid those feelings. The downside is that he or she does not develop the normal capacity to learn from experience. This failure of maturation leads to feelings of inadequacy and depression. Those feelings are then further treated through self-medication in one way or another - and so the process is perpetuated.

Damaging behaviour is repeated because there is no awareness of its consequences: the self-protecting mechanism of feeling appropriate pain is suppressed. This process is reversed in recovery. Meetings of the Anonymous Fellowships enable feelings to be processed in a supportive environment. The Twelve Step programme sets the recovering addict on the path of humility and honesty, the opposite of previous attitudes and behaviour. Abstinence from substances, processes and relationships that alter the mood removes the numbing anaesthesia and enables lessons to be learnt through emotional experience. Each emotional experience is tied into the behaviour that produced it. Maturity comes from learning to make appropriate choices in the light of those emotional experiences that are no longer suppressed by the anaesthesia of addiction. Increasing self-worth, from having the courage to change, enables appropriate feelings to be experienced in response to varying circumstances. The general sense of inner emptiness lifts without the need for anti-depressants or psychotherapy. Even Compulsive Helpers (who use themselves as drugs to help other people) are enabled to be free of their neediness and depressed feelings when they learn to process their feelings appropriately and take responsibility for their own thoughts, feelings, actions and reactions rather than those of other people.

5. Doctors tend to cling to narrow concepts of disease, despite the term's derivation from dis-ease. This reluctance to modify their perception tends to be based upon inertia: they may not know what else to do if they are deprived of their standard (usually medicinal) therapies. They may even become highly critical of patients who are manifestly in great need of help to protect them from progressive self-destruction. Doctors may extol the virtues of control to the very people who have quite clearly eventually lost it after trying too hard to attain it. They may resent the appropriation of the word "disease" by people whom they consider simply to be self-indulgent. They point critically to addiction as not a "real" disease, despite the fact that its consequences often lead to very real diseases indeed. They may try to restrict the definition of disease, or limit the time and attention that they would give to addicts, not realising that in doing so they undermine much of their own rationale for their daily work. Their cynical description of addiction applies as much to many other clinical conditions:

"self-inflicted"	:sports injuries.
"a personal responsibility"	:contraception.
"a social problem"	:unemployment.
"an emotional problem"	:bereavement.
"self-limiting"	:viral infections.
"untreatable"	:Huntington's Chorea

In any other clinical condition doctors would do whatever they could to focus on treating the cause rather than tidying up the consequences. However, in addictive disease, a major contributor to morbidity and mortality, the medical profession tends to be determinedly inactive and dismissive of the sufferers.

6. Psychologists and psychiatrists tend to want to look behind addictive disease, postulating social or psychological causes for it, rather than looking straight at it. Vast numbers of people have had similar social or psychological backgrounds yet have not become addicts. Those ideas simply don't wash: addicts are born, not made. "Letting them off the hook for their behaviour" is the most uninformed of all criticisms of the belief that addictive disease itself is not the fault of the sufferer. Step

IV (Made a full and fearless inventory of ourselves) and Step IX (Made direct amends wherever possible to those we had harmed, except when to do so would injure them or others) of the Anonymous Fellowships do not exactly let addicts "off the hook". Critics should try those steps for themselves.

7. As an ideal general principle, doctors do not moralise but simply deal with the patient's medical condition, or its consequences. However, because of their own fear or disgust, and the general lack of understanding of addictive disease, this reluctance to moralise is frequently forgotten where addicts are concerned.

8. When addicts say "I have tried repeatedly to give up but am drawn back by a compulsion", they are telling the truth. They need to be heard rather than simply dismissed. Observing their other talents and achievements in life would soon give the lie to any perception of them as weak-willed or stupid. In fact addicts themselves are most self-critical in this respect and vast numbers of suicides are evidence of that. The Samaritans estimate that one-third of all suicides are by alcoholics. Add in all other forms of addiction, and the awareness of what is really in the addict's mind becomes plain to see: self-hatred and despair. This needs help rather than a further push towards the abyss.

9. The initial rejection but subsequent gradual understanding of addictive disease has historical precedent. Sufferers from diabetes, thyroid deficiency and epilepsy have all been considered mad, or even inhabited by demons, at some time in the past, even in this century. Addictive disease is simply the next in a long line of adjustments that society at large, and the medical profession in particular, have to make to their perceptions.

10. Addictive disease can justifiably be called a "spiritual" disease because:

i. the primary disease leads to a disorder of mood with a poor self-image and a sense of shame and unworthiness. It is this disorder of the human spirit that leads the sufferer to seek mood-altering substances, processes or relationships;

ii. it gets better with the "spiritual" treatment of the Anonymous Fellowships. Meetings can be described but precisely why the process works is not known in scientific terms, although it is probably through auto-stimulation of our own neurotransmitters through the mood-altering process of reaching out to help another addict. Similarly, science may describe what electricity, gravity or radiation do and we can use them reliably in practical applications, but we still may not be able to describe precisely what each of them is;

iii. sufferers feel better and are temporarily relieved of their urge to use an addictive substance or behaviour after a meeting of an appropriate Anonymous Fellowship. Involvement in a meeting is a "spiritual" process: it is not simply mental, educational or emotional, nor does it merely provide group support, although there are elements of all of these factors. Essentially, active involvement in a Fellowship meeting and in working the Twelve Step programme reverses the characteristics of the disease, giving a sense of peace, hope, trust, love and other positive senses. Repeated involvement in meetings and working the Twelve Steps leads to progressive erosion of the personality traits of addictive disease. Discontinuation of involvement in meetings and stopping working the Twelve Steps leads to recurrence;

iv. it is not primarily a mental disease. The thought processes return to being perfectly intact in those who are in substantial recovery through working the Twelve Step programme of the Anonymous Fellowships. Thus the "stinking thinking" of addictive disease is reversible;

v. it does not respond fully successfully to other forms of mental or emotional treatment such as analytical psychotherapy, behaviour therapy or general psychiatric group therapy, although any of these may possibly be helpful in dealing with other issues once the primary disease is in recovery through the Anonymous Fellowships;

vi. treating the consequences has no effect on the primary "spiritual" disease. Frequently, the consequences are misdiagnosed and treated as causes. This is as inappropriate as expecting a psychologist or psychiatrist to treat the disturbed thought processes of someone in pain from acute gout;

vii. addictive disease has characteristic signs, a typical course of progression and predictable consequences. When the primary "spiritual" disease is treated through the Anonymous Fellowships, all these signs and consequences of addictive disease gradually resolve.

11. There is no evidence that addiction (other than mere physiological addiction) develops as a result of excessive use. Many sufferers from addictive disease describe their very first exposure to a mood-altering substance, process or relationship as being a special, profound, almost magical experience. They state their belief that they were aware of a special relationship with that substance or behaviour from then onwards. Nonetheless, it is true that the addiction is to mood-alteration rather than simply to one substance or behaviour and that, as tolerance develops, progressively more of the substance or behaviour is required to produce the mood-altering effect. In alcoholism this is not the same as saying that sufferers from alcoholism always get drunk: their increased tolerance may enable them to obtain the mood-altering effect but still not be obviously drunk even though they may have consumed significantly more than other people can consume before being obviously drunk. Correspondingly, recreational drug addicts or addicts of any kind may have huge capacity for their particular addictive substances, processes or relationships without showing immediate ill-effects. Conversely, there are many people who drink excessively and get drunk repeatedly or who go through a phase of recreational drug use, gambling, cigarette smoking, bingeing or enforced vomiting or other behaviour that may be similar to that of addictive disease but they can nonetheless stop these processes when they decide to do so and not be inexorably drawn back to addictive substances or behaviours. Those people do not have addictive disease: they may simply have become physiologically addicted and their behaviour may have been self-indulgent rather than compulsive.

12. There is no direct evidence that all people have the potential for addictive disease. There is considerable evidence (for example, from Scandinavian adoption studies and from studies of Vietnam war veterans) that addictive disease only affects particular people, albeit an enormous number. Those of us who have it have to learn what it is and what to do about it.

Genetics

1. Many epidemiological studies, examining large populations over a period of time, already indicate that nature (the way we are made) is a more reliable predictor of addictive or compulsive behaviour than nurture (the way we are brought up and the influence of our various environments). Genetic influence is often considered, or even implied, but it is not yet proven.

2. Professor Ernest Noble of the University of California, Los Angeles, studied the genetic influence on the developing "reward systems" in the mood centres of the brain. He found that in the eleventh human chromosome is a gene that influences the number of receptors of dopamine, a "neurotransmitter" chemical substance that transmits electrical activity from one nerve cell to another. Those people who are found to have fewer dopamine receptors commonly developed excessive appetites for alcohol, nicotine, cocaine, caffeine and sugar. These substances have mood-altering properties that transiently make up for the defect of nature.

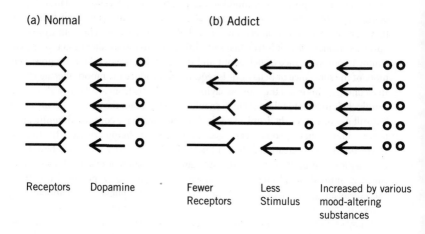

(a) Normal   (b) Addict

Receptors   Dopamine   Fewer   Less   Increased by various
                         Receptors   Stimulus   mood-altering
                                                     substances

3. Recreational and pharmaceutical drugs act on neurotransmitters in various ways, such as increasing or decreasing their output or reception or through blocking their reabsorption.

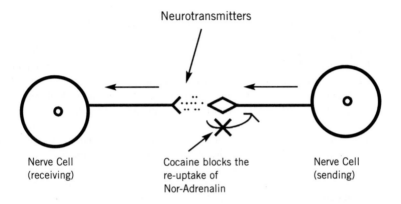

Neurotransmitters

Nerve Cell
(receiving)

Cocaine blocks the
re-uptake of
Nor-Adrenalin

Nerve Cell
(sending)

4. The best known neurotransmitters are Dopamine, Serotin, Nor-Adrenalin and Gamma Amino Butyric Acid. Many pharmaceutical drugs are specifically designed to influence the actions of these particular neurotransmitters. However, over sixty neurotransmitters have already been identified and the total number is thought to be over two thousand. Thus, we really have very little idea of precisely what effect various drugs actually have on the delicate tissues and mechanisms of the brain.

5. Perhaps the tendency towards addiction to many mood-altering substances or processes will come in time to be defined as "neurotransmission disease", comparable to other inborn errors of body function. The sufferers may be born with a defect in mood, feeling agitated or depressed by nature. They then discover, through environmental influence, various substances or processes that improve or control these feelings. Once discovered, never forgotten. Furthermore, most sufferers usually discover several different stimuli that help them to feel "normal" or, at times, to be elated. But the effect wears off and further stimulus is required... and so the addiction is perpetuated.

6. Of course, mood-altering pharmaceutical drugs (painkillers, sleeping tablets, tranquillisers or anti-depressants) are addictive to people who have an addictive tendency. The mood centres of the brain (as opposed to the thinking centres) do not distinguish between legality, illegality, prescription medicines or even mood-altering foods, such as sugar and refined (white) flour, nor even between mood-altering processes such as shopping, spending, stealing, gambling or risk-taking, over-exercising, overworking, bingeing, vomiting or starving, using sex purely for individual mood alteration rather than mutual enhancement, relationship addiction (the need to be "fixed": using other people as if they were drugs) and compulsive helping (the need to be needed: using one's self as a drug for other people).

The mood centres are concerned solely with whether something (anything) has a mood-altering effect.

7. All addictive behaviour is progressive and destructive, with damaging consequences. Eventually the addict cannot live with it but still cannot perceive life without it. At this time the discovery of the Anonymous Fellowships is life-saving. The process of reaching out to help another sufferer anonymously has a mood-altering effect that is constructive rather than destructive. In the Anonymous Fellowships, the continuing genetic defect of the addictive tendency is countered on a continuing daily basis in the same way that many other chronic medical conditions are treated on a continuing daily basis rather than once and for all.

8. There is no shame nor blame in being an addict, only in our behaviour towards other people. The defect of perception (denial), not seeing that one is an addict, is as much a part of the illness as the defect of mood. It has no rational explanation to other people but is very real for the sufferer. Only another addict can understand, from experience, and only another addict can help, because only another addict will be trusted.

9. Love, education and punishment do not work in countering addictive or compulsive behaviour because they cannot fight the genetic predisposition. The Anonymous Fellowships work on a day to day basis, keeping addictive disease in remission, precisely because they provide the mood-altering stimulus of reaching out to help another addict and because they counter the denial by showing the sufferer his reflection in the mirror of the group.

10. Genes may miss a generation (through being recessive rather than dominant). They are not inevitably handed on. Particular addictive outlets often vary between generations. There is a great deal that can be done for those families most at risk. They can be helped to understand the nature of addictive or compulsive behaviour and also the processes involved in prevention of overt addiction or in continuing recovery from it.

The PROMIS Questionnaires

Alcohol

Four positive answers indicate the need for further assessment.

1. I have found that feeling light-headed has often been irrelevant in deciding when to stop drinking alcohol.
2. I have found that having one drink tended not to satisfy me but made me want more.
3. I have had a complete blank of ten minutes or more in my memory when trying to recall what I was doing after drinking alcohol on the previous day or night.
4. I have used alcohol as both a comfort and a strength.
5. I have tended to gulp down the first alcoholic drink fairly fast.
6. I have had a good head for alcohol so that others appeared to get drunk more readily than I did.
7. I have found it strange to leave half a glass of alcoholic drink.
8. I have been irritable and impatient if there has been more than ten minutes conversation at a meal or social function before my host offered me an alcoholic drink.
9. I have deliberately had an alcoholic drink before going out to a place where alcohol may not be available.
10. I have often drunk significantly more alcohol than I intended to.

Recreational Drugs

Four positive answers indicate the need for further assessment.

1. I have particularly enjoyed getting a really strong effect from recreational drugs.
2. I have had a sense of increased tension and excitement when I knew that I had the opportunity to get some drugs.
3. Other people have expressed repeated serious concern about some aspects of my drug use.
4. I have found that getting high tends to result in my going on to take more drugs.
5. I have tended to use drugs as both a comfort and a strength.
6. I have often found that I used all the drugs in my possession even though I had intended to spread them out over several occasions.
7. I have tended to make sure that I have the drugs, or the money for drugs, before concentrating on other things.
8. I have been irritable and impatient if my supply of drugs has been delayed for ten minutes for no good reason.
9. I have tended to use more drugs if I have got more.
10. I have deliberately used drugs before going out if I felt there might not be the opportunity to use them later.

Food Bingeing

Four positive answers indicate the need for further assessment.

1. I have tended to think of food not so much as a satisfier of hunger but as a reward for all the stress I endure.
2. I have tended to use food as both a comfort and a strength even when I have not been hungry.
3. I have found that being full has often been irrelevant in deciding when to stop eating.
4. I have found that I have sometimes put on weight even when I am trying to diet.
5. Other people have expressed repeated serious concern about my excessive eating.
6. I have often preferred to eat alone rather than in company.
7. When I have definitely eaten too much I have tended to feel defiant as well as disappointed in myself.
8. I have preferred to graze like a cow throughout the day rather than ever allow myself to get hungry.
9. I have had three or more different sizes of clothes in my adult (non-pregnant if female) wardrobe.
10. I have been aware that once I have consumed certain foods I have found it difficult to control further eating.

Food Starving

Four positive answers indicate the need for further assessment.

1. In a restaurant or even at home I have often tried to persuade others to choose dishes that I knew I would like, even though I would probably refuse to eat them.
2. When I have eaten in company I have liked to be with special friends or family members whom I can rely upon to finish off some foods for me.
3. I have a list of so many things that I dare not eat that there has been very little left that I can eat.
4. I have often chewed something and then taken it out of my mouth and thrown it away.
5. I have particularly enjoyed eating raw vegetables and also salty or sour things.
6. When I have eaten in company I have tended to time my eating as a form of strategy so that others are not really aware of just how little I am eating.
7. When I have eaten something reasonably substantial I have tended to feel disappointed or even angry with myself as well as slightly relieved.
8. I have become irritable and impatient at meal times if someone has tried to persuade me to eat something.
9. I have often avoided meal times by claiming that I have already eaten when it is not true.
10. Some food has made me wish I could eat it as other people do but I have nonetheless found that I could not bring myself to do so.

Nicotine

Four positive answers indicate the need for further assessment.

1. I have preferred to use nicotine throughout the day rather than only at specific times.
2. I have tended to use nicotine as both a comfort and a strength even when I felt that I did not want any.
3. I have been afraid that I will put on excessive amounts of weight, or become particularly irritable or depressed, if I give up using nicotine altogether.
4. I have often found that my first use of nicotine in any day has tended not to satisfy me but made me want more.
5. I have continued to use nicotine even when I have had a bad cold or a more serious respiratory problem.
6. I have found that my nicotine consumption has gone up or down when I am off alcohol or drugs or when I am on a diet.
7. I have deliberately used nicotine before going out to a place where I may not be able to use it.
8. When I ran out of my favourite form of nicotine, I have accepted the offer of an alternative that I did not particularly like.
9. I have often used nicotine to calm my nerves.
10. I have often used nicotine significantly more than I intended.

Caffeine

"Caffeine" includes coffee, tea, chocolate, cola, lemonade and Pro-plus.

Four positive answers indicate the need for further assessment.

1. I have an intimate relationship with caffeine so that in a strange way I have felt that I became a real person only when I used it.
2. I have preferred to take caffeine on my own rather than in company.
3. I have felt that it would be more painful for me to give up caffeine than to give up a close friendship.
4. I have regularly stolen or helped myself to other people's caffeine even though I had enough money to buy my own.
5. I have tended to time my intake of caffeine so that others are not really aware of my total intake.
6. I have had a sense of increased tension and excitement when I have bought caffeine substances or when I saw advertisements for them.
7. I have found that my intake of another form of caffeine has tended to increase when I am off my own favourite.
8. When I have used too much caffeine I have tended to feel defiant as well as disappointed in myself.
9. I have sometimes rushed through a meal or skipped it altogether so that I could have some caffeine.

10. I have often been capable of drinking twenty cups of tea or coffee or cola or lemonade or eating twenty chocolates in a day.

Gambling and Risk-Taking

"Gambling and risk-taking" includes property ventures, stocks and shares, insurance and other business risks.

Four positive answers indicate the need for further assessment.

1. I have found that the amount that I have won or lost has often been irrelevant in deciding when to stop gambling or risk-taking.
2. I have stolen or embezzled to cover gambling losses or to cover my losses in risky ventures.
3. I have found it more painful to give up gambling and risk-taking than to give up a close friendship.
4. Other people have expressed repeated serious concern over my gambling or risk-taking.
5. I have tended to accept opportunities for further gambling or risk-taking despite having just completed a session or project.
6. I have preferred to gamble or to take risks in one way or another throughout the day rather than at particular times.
7. I have tended to use gambling or risk-taking as a form of comfort and strength even when I have not felt that I particularly wanted to gamble or to take further risks.
8. I have gambled or taken risks at the first opportunity to do so in case I did not get the chance later on.
9. When my favourite form of gambling or risk-taking is unavailable I have gambled on something else I normally disliked.
10. I have been irritable and impatient if there has been a complete break of ten minutes in a gambling session.

Work

"Work" includes hobbies and interests, cults or sects.

Four positive answers indicate the need for further assessment.

1. I have taken on work that I actively disliked, not so much out of necessity but more simply to keep myself occupied.
2. I have tended to work faster and for longer hours than other people of my own ability so that they have found it difficult to keep up with me.
3. When I have definitely overworked and got myself irritable and overtired I have tended to feel defiant as well as slightly ashamed.
4. I have tended to tidy up the mess that someone else has got into at work, even when I have not been asked to do so.

5. I have found that finishing a specific project is often irrelevant in deciding when to stop working.
6. When working with others I have tended to disguise the full amount of time and effort that I put into my work.
7. I have tended to keep reserve projects up my sleeve just in case I find some time, even a few minutes, to spare.
8. I have regularly covered other people's work and responsibilities even when there was no need for me to do so.
9. Other people have expressed repeated serious concern over the amount of time I spend working.
10. I have found that once I start work it has been difficult to get "out of the swing of it" and relax.

Sex and Love Addiction

Four positive answers indicate the need for further assessment.

1. I have found it difficult to pass over opportunities for casual or illicit sex.
2. Other people have expressed repeated serious concern over my sexual behaviour.
3. I have prided myself on the speed with which I can get to have sex with someone and I have found that sex with a complete stranger is stimulating.
4. I have taken opportunities to have sex despite having just had it with somebody else.
5. I have found that making a sexual conquest has caused me to lose interest in that partner and led me to begin looking for another.
6. I have tended to ensure that I have had sex of one kind or another rather than wait for my regular partner to be available after an illness or absence.
7. I have had repeated affairs even though I had a regular relationship.
8. I have had three or more regular sexual partners at the same time.
9. I have had voluntary sex with someone I dislike.
10. I have tended to change partners if sex becomes repetitive.

Prescription Drug Addiction

"Prescription medications" includes all medicines that have a mood-altering effect, especially tranquillisers, anti-depressants, sleeping tablets and pain-killers.

Four positive answers indicate the need for further assessment.

1. I have felt an increased tension or awareness when it has come to the time when I normally take my prescription medication.
2. Other people have expressed repeated serious concern about my use of prescription medication.
3. I have taken more than the prescribed dose of my prescription medication as and when I have felt it necessary.
4. If my prescription medication supply was being strictly controlled, I would hang on to some old prescription medicines even if they were definitely beyond

their expiry date.

5. Other people (e.g. doctors) have commented that they would be knocked out by a fraction of the prescription medication that I have regularly taken.

6. I have found that my previous doses of prescription medicines have no longer been successful in controlling my symptoms.

7. I have continued to take prescription medication because I have found that it helps me, even though the original stresses for which the medication was prescribed have been resolved.

8. If I had run out of my prescription medication I would take an alternative even if I was not sure of its effects.

9. I have been irritable and impatient if my prescription medication has been delayed for ten minutes.

10. I have often found myself taking more prescription medication than I intended to.

Exercise

Four positive answers indicate the need for further assessment.

1. I have often been so tired with exercise that I have found it difficult to walk or to climb up stairs.

2. I have preferred to exercise alone rather than in company.

3. I have often tried to take exercise several times a day.

4. I have particularly enjoyed getting wringing wet with sweat when I exercise.

5. I have often felt a sense of tension and excitement when about to take exercise.

6. I have often responded positively to an unexpected invitation to exercise despite having just finished my regular exercise.

7. I have felt that I become a real person only when I am exercising.

8. I have tended to use exercise as both a comfort and a strength even when I have been perfectly fit and do not need any more.

9. I have often taken exercise just to tire myself sufficiently for sleep.

10. When I have gone out I have often taken sports clothes and equipment with me "just in case" the opportunity to exercise arises.

Shopping/Spending/Stealing

Four positive answers indicate the need for further assessment.

1. I have felt uncomfortable when shopping with other people because it has restricted my freedom.

2. I have particularly enjoyed buying bargains so that I have often finished up with more than I need.

3. I have tended to use shopping and spending as both a comfort and strength even when I do not need anything.

4. I have tended to go shopping just in case I might see something I want.

5. When I have been shopping with family members, friends or other people, I have tended to disguise the full extent of my purchases.

6. I have often bought so many goods (groceries, sweets, household goods, books etc.) that it would take a month to get through them.
7. I have preferred to keep my shopping supplies topped up in case of war or natural disaster, rather than let my stocks run low.
8. I have bought things not so much as a means of providing necessities but more as a reward that I deserve for the stress that I endure.
9. I have felt that I become a real person only when shopping or spending.
10. I have often gone shopping to calm my nerves.

Addictive Relationships

Dominant

Four positive answers indicate the need for further assessment.

1. I have tended to look for, or take on, positions of power or influence so that I rise to a position of emotional or practical power over others as rapidly as possible.
2. I have found it difficult not to take up a position of power or influence when it is available, even when I did not really need it and could see no particular use for it.
3. I have preferred to have power and influence in all my relationships rather than allow myself to be vulnerable.
4. I have been afraid that my life would fall apart and that others would take advantage of me if I were to give up the power and influence that I have held or now hold.
5. I have regularly undermined other people's positions of power or influence even though they may have significantly less than I do.
6. I have found that having all the power and influence that I needed for my own personal and professional life has been irrelevant in deciding when to stop seeking more.
7. I have tended to use a position of power or influence as a comfort and strength regardless of whether there have been particular problems needing my attention in other aspects of my life.
8. I have looked for all opportunities for power and influence as and when they arise.
9. In a new relationship I have felt uncomfortable until I hold the most powerful position.
10. I have tended to neglect other aspects of my life when I have felt that my position of power or influence has been under threat.

Submissive.

Four positive answers indicate the need for further assessment.

1. I have tended to be upset when someone close to me has taken care of someone else.
2. I have felt that I become a real person only when I am being totally looked after by someone else.
3. I have found that other people have tended to express progressively more

concern about my dependent relationships.

4. I have tended to find someone else to be close to me when my primary partner has been away even for a short time.
5. I have tended to find a new close relationship within days or weeks of the failure of a previous one.
6. I have tended to venture into company only if I have someone to look after me.
7. I have felt an overwhelming sense of excitement when I have found a new person to look after my needs or a new way in which an existing partner could look after them better.
8. I have tended to think that a close friendship is when someone else really looks after me.
9. I have tended to get irritable and impatient when people look after themselves rather than me.
10. I have felt most in control of my feelings when other people are performing services of one kind or another for me.

Compulsive Helping

Dominant

Four positive answers indicate the need for further assessment.

1. I have been afraid that I would be thought of as (and perhaps become) a callous person if I do not show my capacity for self-denial and caretaking on a daily basis.
2. The things I have done for others have often resulted in there being not much left of my personal life.
3. I have preferred to look after other people on my own rather than as part of a team.
4. I have found life rather empty when someone for whom I was caring gets better and I have felt resentful at times when I am no longer needed.
5. I have tended to use my self-denial and caretaking as both a comfort and strength for myself.
6. I have found that I tend to adopt a self-denying and caretaking role in many of my relationships.
7. I have regularly given unsolicited advice to other people on how to solve their problems.
8. I have found it difficult to leave any loose ends in a conversation in which I am trying to be helpful.
9. I have often stayed up half the night having "helpful" conversations.
10. I have felt that I become a real person only when I am tidying up the physical, emotional and social messes made by someone else.

Submissive

Four positive answers indicate the need for further assessment.

1. I have tended to pride myself on never being a burden to others.

2. Other people have tended to express concern that I am not doing enough for my own pleasure.
3. I have tried to avoid all risks of upsetting other people.
4. I have tended to give (an act of service to others) and not count the costs even though the costs mount progressively.
5. I have tended to remain loyal and faithful regardless of what I may endure in a close relationship.
6. I have liked to make myself useful to other people even when they do not appreciate what I do.
7. I have tended to take on more work for someone close to me even if I have not finished the previous batch.
8. I have felt like a real person only when performing acts of service for someone else.
9. I have often helped someone close to me more than I intended.
10. I have felt most in control of my feelings when performing services of one kind or another for someone else.

Compulsive Helping in People who are also Addicts

Four positive answers indicate the need for further assessment.

1. I have kept other addicts' secrets or covered up for them and therefore, through their dishonesty, made their relapse more probable.
2. I have protected other addicts from the consequences of their behaviour.
3. Through my own self-denial, I have allowed myself to be dragged down in a direction in which I did not really want to go.
4. I have risked my own recovery in the process of "helping" another addict.
5. I have tried to lessen the feelings (sadness, fear, anger and loneliness) that other addicts experience as a result of their addictive behaviour rather than letting them learn from their experience.
6. I have deliberately blurred the distinction between normal helping and compulsive helping in order to ridicule compulsive helping or avoid facing up to its truly destructive nature.
7. I have sometimes deliberately misunderstood the difference between people pleasing (wanting popularity), compulsive helping (the need to be needed) and primary addictive relationships (using other people as if they were drugs).
8. I have used compulsive helping as a means of controlling my own feelings.
9. Through care-taking for other people, I have focused my attention on their behaviour while avoiding looking at my own compulsive helping.
10. I have failed to support other people in confronting addicts over their behaviour.

Identifying Addiction and Preventing Relapse

1. Addiction and relapse are identical. The quality of our recovery can always be improved but we cannot be partially in recovery: we are either in recovery or we are not. Relapse is a process that begins long before the event of actual return to a specific addictive substance, process or relationship. From the moment we cease to work actively for our recovery on a continuing daily basis, we move into relapse.

2. Lists of "warning signs" of relapse behaviour are already too late: by the time that they are relevant, the process is already under way and the probability is that nothing other than a really sharp shock will stop it and restore our sanity. Just as when we first came into recovery, the only thing that persuades us to change our behaviour is pain: when we perceive that the pain of continuing as we are will be worse than the pain of changing.

3. To reduce the risk of relapse we need to look at all addictive outlets: alcohol, nicotine, caffeine, "recreational" drugs, mood-altering prescription drugs, workaholism, exercise addiction, compulsive shopping or spending or stealing, compulsive gambling or risk-taking, bingeing, starving, vomiting or purging food, sex and love addiction (using these activities purely for mood-altering effect rather than to create a deeper relationship), relationship addiction (the need to be "fixed": using other people as if they were drugs) and compulsive helping (the need to be needed: using ourselves as drugs for other people).

4. Within each addiction we need to look at specific addictive characteristics: preoccupation with use or non-use; preference for (or contentment with) use alone; use as a medicine to help relax or sedate or to stimulate; use primarily for mood-altering effect; protection of "supply" (preferring to spend time, energy or money in this way); repeatedly using more than planned because the first use tends to trigger the next; having a higher capacity than other people for using the substance or process without obvious initial damaging effects (although in time this "tolerance" is lost); continuing to use despite progressively damaging consequences; "drug-seeking" behaviour (looking for opportunities to use an addictive substance or behaviour in order to function effectively); "drug-dependent" behaviour (functioning better when using the addictive substance or behaviour); the tendency to "cross-addict" into other addictive substances or behaviours when we attempt to control our use; and continuing to use despite the repeated serious concern of other people.

5. Addictions tend to come in groups, although alcohol can come in either of the first two groups:
   i.   "hedonistic": recreational drugs, prescription drugs, nicotine, caffeine, gambling and risk-taking, sex and love addiction, "dominant" relationships (that threaten to "harm" the other person).
   ii. "nurturant of self": food (any eating disorder behaviour), workaholism, exercise addiction, compulsive shopping or spending or stealing, "submissive" relationships (that threaten to "harm" oneself).

iii. Compulsive helping.

Some addicts have addictive outlets in just one of these groups, some in two, some in all three. Most addicts have three or four different individual outlets rather than just one. It is appropriate therefore to refer to ourselves generally as "addicts" rather than by the name of any one particular addictive outlet such as "alcoholic" or "workaholic": therein would lie false security, a shallow recovery and a fearful risk of relapse.

Personality Traits of Addictive Disease

1. **Blame:** the sufferer from addictive disease believes that if only other people would change then everything would be all right. Blaming other people, while opting out of responsibility for one's own condition, is the hallmark of an active addict.

2. **Self-pity:** the spiritual isolation, the feeling that the sufferer is "special and different" and misunderstood, results in recurrent thoughts of victimisation.

3. **Denial:** this central psycho-pathology of addictive disease is the process in which the sufferer is "told" by the disease that he or she does not have it. This denial is so intense that other people who are close to the sufferer may come to doubt their own certainty or even their own sanity.

4. **Stubbornness:** addictive disease is closed-minded and not open to persuasion. Why should it be? Other people are perceived to have the problem; not the sufferer.

5. **Self-centredness:** individual will-power, the absolute determination to control the use of addictive substances, processes and relationships, is exactly what perpetuates the disease. The emphasis on control, despite all the evidence that this is precisely what is being progressively lost, focuses the sufferer's mind on self and not upon others. The sufferer becomes the centre of his or her own world, increasingly disregarding relationships with others in the past or future.

6. **Pride:** determined belief in the capacity for self-control results in pride that the sufferer has special standards and abilities that others lack. As standards slip, the determined pride is readjusted to a lower level of behaviour with the assertion "well at least I don't do that". This exaggeration of the sufferer's ability is in compensation for the inner lack of belief in self.

7. **Anger and resentment:** anger is so fundamental to addictive disease that it goes with the person rather than with specific events. Short-term anger is fuelled to become long-term resentment.

8. **Conflict with "authority":** the sufferer genuinely believes that he or she is normal and that the world has problems and therefore so do the people who "run" the world or family.

9. **Procrastination:** the continuing need to demonstrate self-control results in all lesser activities being put off "for the time being".

10. **Perfectionism:** the reason so many things are delayed is that they have to be perfect. Criticising other people for their inadequacies puts a tremendous burden of perfectionism on the sufferer in his or her own activities.

11. **Externalisation:** the poor internal self-image is reflected outwards on to other people and on to external circumstances rather than being recognised as the diseased part of self. Everything is the fault of people or things "out there" rather than "in here".

12. **Intellectualisation:** there is nothing that addictive disease likes more than a circuitous argument in search of absolute proof on precise definitions of addiction. Feelings are suppressed while the head endlessly debates.

Denial

1. Denial (the belief that we do not have a problem when it is obvious to others that we do) is the basic psycho-pathology of addictive disease. It is seen in other clinical conditions, such as acute fear or grief, but is central to the understanding of addictive behaviour. When an addict says that he or she hasn't done something or other, or doesn't have a problem, he or she is telling the truth as perceived. The " truth", however, is incorrect.

2. Denial becomes more intense as addictive disease progresses. The alcoholic sleeping rough does not see that alcohol was ever a cause of his or her problems. The intravenous drug-user can give up at any time, and has done so frequently, and sees nothing incongruous in that statement. The anorexic patient at death's door really believes that he or she has overeaten and is bloated and fat.

3. When the shutters are down there is no way in. One can see the shutters come down, not only as a result of direct use of a mood-altering substance or process but when the addict's mind turns to thoughts of using. When the switch is thrown the lights go out and that's that until the next small window of opportunity presents itself. It is therefore vitally important to catch an addict at the right time when this opportunity of coherent intervention presents itself. There is no point in discussing anything with an addict who is under the influence of any mood-altering substance, including mood-altering prescription medication such as painkillers, sleeping tablets, tranquillisers, anti-depressants and, most of all, Methadone.

4. Addicts have a selective forgetting mechanism. We remember the good feelings that come with the use of addictive substances, processes and relationships but forget the pain and the disastrous consequences that also came with them. At meetings of the Anonymous Fellowships we see ourselves reflected in the mirror of the group.

5. Denial has specific progressive sub-sections as follows:

   i. Simple denial: the straightforward refusal to accept that something is so.
   ii. Minimising: accepting that there are problems but denying their true significance.
   iii. Externalisation or blaming: acknowledging the severity of the problem but finding external causes.
   iv. Rationalisation: finding excuses for one's behaviour.
   v. Intellectualisation: saying "Yes, but…"
   vi. Diversions: saying "My real problem is…"
   vii. Hostility: open attack on any mention of the concept of addiction.

These processes of progressive denial can be seen not only in addicts themselves but also in those close to them and even in society at large when there is any suggestion that addiction is part of "us" rather than "them".

Creativity

1. Being an addict is not all bad news. When we develop a sense of inner emptiness, we are always on the look-out for something to help us to feel better. Our antennae are finely tuned. We learn to be imaginative and to take risks and to be creative.

2. In time, our addictive disease turns our creativity to its own advantage, using all our attributes and skills against us. We find new ways of maintaining our addictive behaviour and of justifying it to ourselves and others. We adjust our values and our lifestyle to accommodate our addiction. We become creatively destructive.

3. In recovery we learn how to reclaim our talents for our own benefit. By maintaining our recovery on a day-to-day basis we can even have the last laugh on our addictive disease: we can turn all its manipulations to our own future advantage. We know all the tricks of the trade and can now use them constructively.

4. Strangely, we often fear that we will lose our creativity if we give up using addictive substances, processes or relationships. This may be true initially when we are getting over the addictive process of "state dependent learning" (being able to function best when we are in the same state as when we learnt that activity) but subsequently we are far more creative in recovery then we ever were before.

5. The full wealth of human emotion that addicts endure or enjoy becomes the well-spring of future creativity. We fought against accepting that we are addicts and we carry the scars of that futile battle. Subsequently we worked, without fear or favour, for our recovery and we deserve the fruits of our labours.

6. When at last our minds are at peace, and our relationships happily settled and

mutually supportive, we can draw on our familiarity with a whole kaleidoscope of colour in our feelings and turn this experience towards creative output.

7. In the richness of our recovery we discover that there is one thing above all else that is worthy of our entire creative capacity: living each day to the full and giving the finest expression to the best potential within us.

Courage

is:

being fearful but not being foolhardy.

knowing a true value.

having my own ideas and principles and living by them.

risking my life and everything I have only for something I myself believe in.

daring to make mistakes.

recognising when I am wrong.

taking unfair criticism and cruel turns of fate without bitterness or resentment.

feeling sad without being self-obsessed.

observing other people's success without envy.

ignoring popularity.

practising daily disciplines, regardless of circumstance.

a lonely, private, place.

The Courage to Change

When we are in the grip of our addictive disease, our inner emptiness and determination to control lead to a "King-Baby" state in which grandiosity, self-centredness, blame and self-pity result in an inability to feel any genuine feelings.

In recovery, by letting go and depending upon a higher power than self, we develop the humility, other-people-centredness, understanding of others and acceptance of self that enable us to feel the full range of feelings in response to whatever actually happens in our lives. By gaining the courage to change and the enthusiasm to do so, we use the full range of the tools of recovery to keep our addictive disease in remission on a daily basis.

Addictive Disease

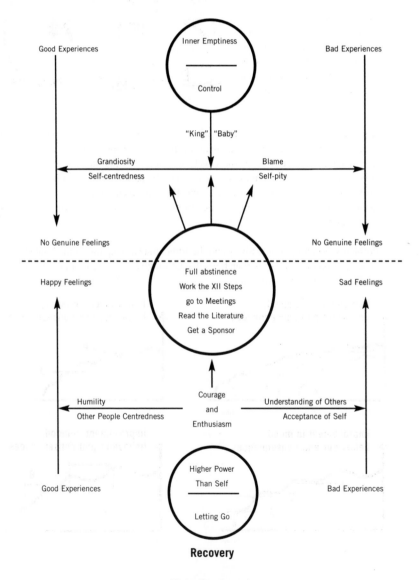

a new life healing depression

The Progression of Addictive Disease

1. Addictive disease is a disease of the human spirit, of hope, love, trust, honour, innocence, and other spiritual values. It is probably genetically inherited and caused by defects of neurotransmission in the chemical on/off switch between electrically activated nerve cells in the mood centres of the brain. The result is a disorder of mood, a profound sense of inner emptiness.

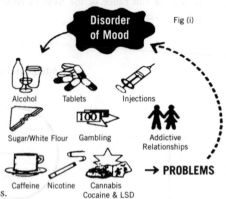

Fig (i)

2. A potential addict discovers for himself or herself the mood-altering properties of some substances, behaviours and relationships. These transiently resolve the mood disorder but it returns when the effects wear off. As the sufferer discovers the effectiveness of these "treatments" he or she returns for more. In time there are problems as a result of repeated use and these problems further exacerbate the disorder of mood. Thus, the cycle continues and addictive behaviour becomes established.

3. Problems mount up progressively and the addict may give up the additive substance, process or relationship - but then finds that although he or she cannot live with it, he or she also cannot live without it.

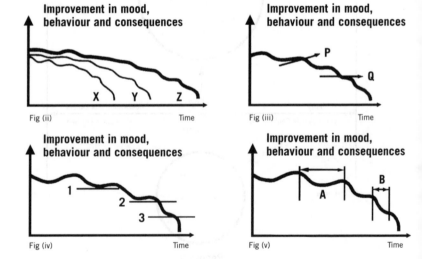

a new life healing depression

4. As with many other genetically-inherited conditions that involve the interaction of a number of genes, the intensity of addictive disease (possibly in future better termed neurotransmission disease) varies in intensity from one sufferer to another (see fig. ii, x, y, z).

5. The progressive deterioration of mood, behaviour and its consequences is a wavy path rather than a straight line. Therefore there are confusing times (see fig iii, P & Q) when things appear to be getting better or at least no worse.

6. The progression is better identified by observing (fig iv) that each crisis is more intense than the last and (fig v) that the crises become more frequent as time progresses.

The Progression of Recovery and Relapse

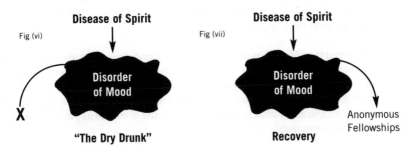

1. Simply abstaining from mood-altering substances, behaviours and relationships (fig vi) results in the "dry drunk" state where the mood disorder and the associated disturbed behaviour may persist even though problems secondarily associated with the specific addictive substances, behaviour or relationship may resolve. Thus, for example, the atrocious mood and behaviour may persist even though drunkenness or other forms of addiction and their specific consequences are no longer present.

2. Family members, colleagues or employers at work, doctors and other personal or professional helpers may find the "dry drunk" state very confusing and make the mistake of assuming that there is an additional problem such as "depression" or that social circumstances need to be changed. Addicts themselves will gladly go along with these suggestions because they appear to confirm that the "real" problem was never really anything to do with addictive substances, processes or relationships in the first place.

3. The correct treatment of the mood disorder of addictive disease is regular attendance at meetings of appropriate Anonymous Fellowships. Their effect wears off, just as the mood-altering effect of substances, behaviour and relationships wears off, so attendance has to be on a repeated basis for life if relapse or the "dry drunk" state is to be avoided.

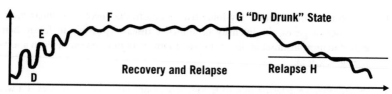

Fig (viii)

4. In early recovery there are frequent wide-ranging fluctuations of mood (fig viii). This may result in two opposite but equivalent risks. At D things feel so awful that there is a risk of abandoning the Twelve Step programme because it is thought to be useless. At E things are going so well that it is thought to be unnecessary.

5. At F, after at least two years of total abstinence from all mood-altering substances, addictive behaviour and addictive relationships, recovery should be securely established, yet there will still be some fluctuations in mood, as with normal people, although probably to a greater extent.

6. At G when the addict takes recovery for granted, and stops going to meetings of the Anonymous Fellowships, the disease reasserts itself and there is deterioration in mood, behaviour and consequences even in the absence of use of addictive substances, behaviour or relationships. This "dry drunk" state, before H, the time of relapse back to active addiction, illustrates addictive disease in its pure form without any of its "treatments".

Intervention

1. "Old timers" sometimes say that addicts have to hit "rock bottom" before they get better. They are wrong. Even in Chapter 1 of "The Twelve Steps and Twelve Traditions" there was rejoicing that those "who were scarcely more than potential alcoholics" joined A.A. Furthermore, how could these "old timers" be sure that an individual's "rock bottom", the time at which he or she is prepared to admit defeat, is not below the mortality line?

2. The Johnson Institute in the USA first developed the principles of intervention, to bring the bottom up to hit the addict, i.e. to make the addict aware of just how uncomfortable life can be right now, let alone in the future.

3. For an addict the use of the addictive substance, process or relationship is the central feature of life, almost its purpose, certainly the only thing that makes it tolerable. The only thing that will change this attitude is pain. The addict therefore needs to see that, if things continue as they are, life will be more painful than if they change. Yet how can change be contemplated when it is perceived as jumping voluntarily into the pit of despair? At this point the encouragement of others who have done the

same, and who have survived and flourished, is vital because it brings a sense of genuine hope.

4. Addictive disease is a disease of mood and also of perception. The disease itself makes us feel a deep sense of inner emptiness. We use addictive substances, processes and relationships to help us to feel better. Yet at the same time, through "denial" (the perception defect) the disease "tells" us that we haven't got it. What a truly fearful disease it is that can do that: progressively killing us while leading us to believe that it is the outside world that causes all the problems rather than our own inside world!

5. To change this perception needs more than the love of family or the advice of well-meaning doctors, employers or friends, or even the punishments of an offended society. Only when all these are harnessed together in structured format, and with absolutely clear choices given and consequences threatened, will the addict be able to listen. Even then he or she will duck and dive, wriggle and prevaricate, and do everything possible to find a weak link so as to divide and rule.

6. Formal interventions therefore have to be planned and rehearsed so that each participant is totally convinced of his or her own powerlessness to get through to the addict on his or her own. Each needs to be reminded of the various attempts which have been made to change the addict's behaviour but which have inevitably failed.

7. At the formal intervention itself, preferably with a specialist Twelve Step addictions counsellor to guide things, each participant says to the addict:
    i.   I love you (or am fond of you)
    ii.   AND (not but) I'm concerned for you.
    iii. These are the things I observe....(facts not opinions)
    iv.   This is what I want you to do...
    v.   and this is what I shall do if you don't....

8. Sometimes it works, sometimes it doesn't, but we need to remember that if we don't take risks now there will be even bigger risks to take later on. If it doesn't work, and the addict doesn't seek help, then the pressure has to be kept on so that the painful consequences accumulate. Don't back out, don't cover up: that kills.

9. Family members, in particular, need support from an appropriate "family" Anonymous Fellowship at this difficult time.

Addiction and the Law

1. Addictive disease is an illness that is not the fault of the sufferer. It has many outlets, some of them legal, some illegal, but ultimately all of them progressive and destructive, not only for the addict but commonly also for those around him or her.

2. Society therefore needs to be protected from the destructive behaviour of addicts. The addicts themselves need to feel the consequences of their behaviour, being punished appropriately when they have harmed other people or their property. Indeed, progressively more painful consequences for using addictive substances, processes and relationships are a necessary part of intervention into addictive disease, ultimately persuading addicts to change their behaviour.

3. In accidents, influenza, heart disease, cancer and other physical diseases, and even in mental illness, we know how to be helpful: we do everything we can to help the sufferer to be free from pain and suffering. If we do that for addicts we make them worse: they carry on exactly as before. We get their pain and that doesn't help them or us. Leaving addicts to endure the full consequences of their actions may be life-saving, however difficult the initial prospect may be for us, as family members, friends or helpers of one kind or another. Making out that things aren't really so bad, telling lies on the addicts' behalf, providing alibis, finding the best available lawyers to defend them, prescribing mood-altering drugs for them, saying that the problems are all due to stress, to difficult environments, or to malign influences - all this makes things worse, not better, for addicts. By avoiding short term pain we get long term agony.

4. Often the most damage to addicts comes from well-meaning attempts to be helpful and supportive, particularly by the State and by helping agencies. Providing free drugs does not prevent crime whereas it does perpetuate the addiction. Providing social support simply removes the responsibility for self. Tidying up the consequences of addictive behaviour simply means that the addicts do not need to do so. It makes no difference whether the addiction is to an illegal substance (a "recreational" drug), a legal substance (nicotine, alcohol), food (sugar and white flour in the eating disorders), or an addictive relationship (using one's self or other people as if we or they were drugs). The guiding principle of intervention is always the same: anything that helps addicts to avoid the painful consequences of their behaviour actually damages rather than helps.

5. The law of the land should be consistent:

   i. The use of any mood-altering substance should be legal, provided that this use does not damage other people. This is the current legal situation for alcohol and nicotine, highly addictive substances that cause immense damage.

   ii. The law, through the Mental Health Act, should protect those who have no insight into the true nature of their own behaviour and should also protect society from them. This situation already applies to schizophrenia and other psychoses and should also apply to all addicts. There is no liberty in compulsive behaviour.

Otherwise, our society is doomed. Present clinical, legal and social approaches have not worked. The problem of addictive disease is here to stay and it is not going to go into remission without severe measures to make it do so. The answer lies not so much in giving the police, customs officers, courts and jails more work to do but in coupling their efforts with a policy of zero tolerance to addictive behaviour and getting would-be helpers out of the way so that addicts get the full consequences of their behaviour and come to seek appropriate treatment for themselves.

Psychotherapy

1. There is nothing that using addicts like more than psychotherapy:

    i.   We like to believe that there is an underlying social cause for all our problems and that someone else is ultimately to blame for our condition.
    ii. We can continue using addictive substances, processes and relationships while we are receiving psychotherapy because we can proclaim to everyone else (and to ourselves) that we are doing something about our problems.
    iii. We can easily manipulate any psychotherapist on a one-to-one basis. All we have to learn from the psychotherapist are a few jargon words, phrases or concepts and the "therapy" can continue for years without either of us ever needing to question our own philosophy.

2. Dr Carl Jung, one of the greatest psychotherapists of all time, acknowledged that there was nothing he could do to help alcoholics. He believed that they needed a spiritual experience. He was impressed by the principles of Alcoholics Anonymous and was a great influence upon the early members.

3. Dr Alfred Adler, another great psychotherapist, said "You can be healed (of depression) if every day you begin, the first thing in the morning, to consider how you can bring a real joy to someone else. If you can stick to this for two weeks you will no longer need therapy".

4. Despite these profound insights, lesser mortals rush in where these great men knew their own limitations. Men and women who have scarcely examined their own behaviour at all, and who may have little experience of life itself or of working closely with others in a therapeutic setting, nonetheless set themselves up as therapists - or even as psychotherapists (the extra "psycho-" enabling higher fees to be charged).

5. Some particular psychotherapeutic approaches, such as searching out early childhood memories, focusing in various ways on pain or anger, or recounting and analysing dreams, can be exceedingly risky: the patient may become as self-centred and boring, and even as damaged, as the psychotherapist.

6. Two psychotherapists will produce four opinions on what is wrong and what needs to be done: each has one opinion of his or her own and another opinion on why the other is wrong. Thus there may be some safety - but also confusion - in numbers. For addicts the safest number of psychotherapists is zero. The Twelve Steps of the Anonymous Fellowships contain all the insight and therapy that is required.

Furthermore, we are actively involved when working the Twelve Steps, whereas in psychotherapy we may be merely passive, soaking up time and concepts while making no practical change.

7. Group therapy has the advantage that the group itself, as a corporate body, has more experience and insight than is containable in any one head. Facilitating a group therapy session requires intuition, inspiration and management skills and also the personal experience of the problems that the group members share in common. However, it also requires the humility to recognise that the group has more therapeutic power than the counsellor, and that patients get better when they are ready to do so. Our function as counsellors in group therapy sessions is solely to practise our professional skills to the best of our ability and leave the rest to the group and to God. There is nothing more that can be asked of us and there is nothing more that we should expect of ourselves. To set up ourselves as psychotherapists - as if we had the power to heal - is dangerous arrogance.

Insight and Intuition

1. Only an addict can have insight into addiction. Other people may have great knowledge about addiction but only addicts understand what it feels like

    i. to have the inner emptiness of addictive disease;
    ii. to despair at our inability to control it solely through our own talents and determination;
    iii. to be inspired by other (recovering) addicts who show us how to use group power to combat individual weakness.

2. Shared experience and personal empathy alone do not give insight and intuition, which are products of the mind and which therefore require hard work.

3. For the mind to work at its peak capacity, it has first to be clear. It cannot be clear while we are still using addictive substances, behaviours or relationships. It will still be preoccupied. Feelings will be confused and resentment will never be far below the surface. While we use any form of addictive substance or process or relationship, we render ourselves little more effective in helping other addicts than people who merely know about addiction from the outside.

4. To say "I know how you feel" is a prodigious assumption. To have shared experience does not necessarily produce the same emotional reactions. The starting position, from childhood experience and present social state, let alone individual and family influences, may be crucially different.

5. However, to sense a particular feeling at a particular time is certainly possible and to be able to do so is a necessary part of professional counselling skills as well as being generally helpful in developing sensitivity in personal relationships. For one mind

(the counsellor's) to resonate with another, the first mind must be clear of junk. Insecurities left over from childhood and earlier adult life should have been processed appropriately, leading to acceptance, understanding and forgiveness. Current use of any mood-altering substance, process and relationship should be as near as possible to zero, although no recovery can be perfect. We can easily put down addictive substances but differentiating between normal and addictive use of a mood-altering process or relationship can be difficult and requires constant examination. Nevertheless, the cleaner we are, the more insight and intuition we gain. The less our minds are cluttered with our own garbage (the burden of self), the more we are able to appreciate the perspectives and idiosyncrasies of others. If we ourselves are clear-headed and at peace, then extraneous thoughts and feelings that pop into our minds will have been picked up intuitively (from body language and many other signals) from the other person.

6. Trainee counsellors, whatever their academic qualifications and however long they have been in recovery in the Anonymous Fellowships, should initially make no contribution whatever to group therapy sessions. No one doubts that they can speak. They need to be able to demonstrate after the session is over that they have heard and observed not only what the participants said and did but also what they did not say and do. Insight and intuition take time to develop.

Minnesota Method Treatment

1. Minnesota Method Treatment is not Alcoholics Anonymous on wheels or in beds: it is a great deal more than that. Counsellors require special training irrespective of how much personal recovery they may have in the Anonymous Fellowships.

2. Residential treatment based upon Twelve Step principles began at the same time in Minnesota in St Mary's Hospital, Minneapolis, where a medical model helped patients to examine their psychological problems and work out what could best be done for them, and in Hazelden, Center City, where a spiritual (non-religious) programme helped patients to acknowledge their powerlessness over addictive behaviour and learn to hand over their lives to God or some other Higher Power than self. The two approaches combined became the Minnesota Method.

3. The sole function of treatment is to help a larger number of people to get better in the Anonymous Fellowships than would otherwise do so. The recovery rate of treatment centres themselves is zero: recovery comes from continuing attendance at meetings of the Anonymous Fellowships and through working the Twelve Step programme.

4. Some patients are so damaged by their addiction that they require initial detoxification under medical supervision. Contrary to popular belief, coming off an addictive substance is relatively straightforward: many addicts do it by themselves many times over, although this may be unsafe in particular in alcoholism and prescription drug addiction, where there may be a risk of epileptic fits in withdrawal.

The real challenge is in learning how to stay off. That is what takes time in treatment.

5. Some patients have multiple addictions. Although it is obviously sensible to deal with the most life-threatening addictions first, it is equally sensible to look at all one's addictive behaviour while in treatment. Why would one want to leave any untreated? The challenge of looking at all addictions (including for example, nicotine addiction, the most pernicious and destructive addiction of all) is difficult but the relapse rate is significantly higher in patients who continue to smoke or who have other persistent active addictions. The concept that it is too much to look at everything all at once is simply "disease talk": addictive disease doing everything it can to maintain its hold as an internal spiritual parasite, ready to strike out and destroy at some time in the future.

6. Most Anonymous Fellowships look at only one addiction whereas most sufferers have three or four or even more addictive outlets. Addictions Anonymous, Narcotics Anonymous and even Cocaine Anonymous allow mention of any addiction. The idea in other Fellowships that to do so "would confuse newcomers" is garbage and often represents a rear-guard action by "old timers" who are reluctant to look at the spread of their own addictive behaviour beyond one substance or process. Time and understanding of addiction have moved on. While it is certainly helpful to be able to identify closely with the experience of other sufferers, the real need is to identify with the underlying addictive process that can come out in any form. By themselves, some Anonymous Fellowships have very poor recovery rates. They have gained a great deal from the perspectives coming back to them from Minnesota Method treatment centres.

7. Conversely, some therapeutic approaches can be very damaging to recovery when they diminish the essential spiritual nature of the recovery programme. If therapeutic - or, for that matter, religious - approaches could have worked by themselves in the treatment of addiction they would have done so years ago. "Therapy" can become an opportunity to blame childhood experiences for our present condition and can look at all sorts of "magic fixes" instead of focusing on the simple straightforward clear disciplines of working the Twelve Steps of the Anonymous Fellowships.

8. Within a treatment centre the opportunity arises for all forms of therapeutic approaches to be tried - because individual patients respond best in different ways, some to reading and writing, some to pictorial collages, some to psychodrama and so on - but it is the variety itself, rather than any specific approach, that is helpful. This variety of therapeutic approaches in group therapy also diminishes the influence of individual crackpot counsellors.

9. The essential therapeutic tool in treatment centres is time. It takes time for the brain to clear. It takes time to understand the nature of addictive disease and recovery. It takes time to emerge from isolation and bond with others (which is why traditionally bedrooms are shared: much of the "work" in treatment centres occurs

after the staff have gone home). It takes time to deal with blocks to recovery such as difficulties with grief, guilt and shame, and it takes time out of our customary disturbed environments to learn a new perspective on life.

10. The introduction to the Twelve Steps is treatment centres is merely a basic familiarisation, because it takes two years to go through the grief reaction that is inherent in Step I alone. Some treatment centres focus on the first three or five steps but this runs the risk of patients believing that those steps have been "done". The further risk is that the recovering addicts never get round to looking at the remaining steps in any depth. It is a better principle to provide some familiarity with all the Twelve Steps and an awareness that these have to be worked, each in turn, in greater depth in the future if we are to gain recovery in any depth, rather than mere abstinence.

11. Most importantly, the focus on group work rather than one-to-one counselling (which can be disastrous because it may lead to a fixation on "the only person who understands me", a process that can be equally destructive to both patient and counsellor) enables patients to see themselves reflected in the mirror of the group. This group work combats "denial", the psycho-pathology in which addicts simply do not see their own disturbed thoughts and behaviour.

12. Family programmes in treatment centres enable family members or "significant others" to gain an understanding of their own difficulties, and acknowledge their own pain, as well as coming to understand addictive processes and thereby see their loved ones in a new light. Relationships can be helped to gain a fresh start, if that is what the participants want, or to end in a dignified and constructive manner if not.

13. Aftercare programmes should never be a substitute for attendance at meetings of the Anonymous Fellowships but they can maintain the intense bonds of friendship established during treatment as well as providing the opportunity to show newcomers (fresh form treatment) that recovery is a continuing process that works in improving the quality of life and that it can also be a lot of fun.

Paradoxes

Addicts use mood-altering substances, processes and relationships because we use them: the first use in any day triggers the need for more. We say that we will use just once - forgetting what happened the last time we used just once. We claim to be special and different when we actually behave exactly like any other addict. We demand to be obeyed as kings but also nurtured as babies. Eventually we cannot live with our addiction but cannot live without it. We ask for help but, in the same breath, push it away. We say that we know what we don't know. We say there is no God and thereby we make our own intellect our God.

"I could not help myself until I realised that I could not help myself." This simple paradox concerning recovery from addictive disease is only explained when the emphasis is placed on the third "I". We receive the gift of recovery only when we recognise that we are powerless to help ourselves: when we surrender.

"We keep what we give away" is another paradox that explains that we receive help ourselves only in the process of reaching out to help others.

In order to rid ourselves of continuing suffering, we learn paradoxically not to look at those who have harmed us but at those we ourselves have harmed.

In order to change the pattern of the whole of our future lives we learn to follow the paradoxical advice to change our behaviour for just one day at a time.

Everywhere we look in addictive disease and recovery we are beset by paradoxes. No wonder addictive disease is so difficult to understand. No wonder recovery is so difficult to achieve. In active addiction we treat our friends as enemies when they try to help us to stop using addictive substances and processes and try to show us the damage we are doing to ourselves as well as to others. Correspondingly, we treat our "enemies" as friends, when they encourage us towards further addictive use and destruction.

Throughout all this carnage the disease "tells" us that we have not got it: addictive disease affects our perception. When we say that we cannot see that we have a problem, we are telling the truth - but our truth is false.

When our families and friends and various "helping" professionals do whatever they can to relieve our pain, even to the extent of suffering considerable pain themselves, they help us to avoid facing up to the full consequences of our behaviour and this takes us further into our disease. The helping professionals, paradoxically, are the least likely source of help for addicts of any kind. The truly effective help for the physical, mental, emotional and social ravages of addictive disease is the spiritual process of working a Twelve Step programme alongside other recovering addicts.

Counselling

1. Counsellors who call themselves therapists or psychotherapists, or who become convinced of the therapeutic effectiveness of particular psychotherapeutic approaches, as opposed to the Twelve Steps in the treatment of addictive disease, have a high incidence of relapse. Their pretentiousness is bad news for addicts and for themselves. Charisma in a counsellor can be inspirational but it can also be the opposite of the essential Step III process of getting rid of the burden of self.

2. Counsellors are easily manipulated by addicts in one-to-one sessions, which is precisely why addicts like them so much. Addicts don't want to be exposed to the full scrutiny of the group. We want someone to acknowledge not just our individuality (which is appropriate) but that we are "special and different" and need

particular individual care (which we don't). By flattering a counsellor, learning some therapeutic jargon, and by talking about our childhood experiences and shedding a few tears, we gain control and need never again look at our own responsibility for our own condition.

3. In particular, in one-to-one sessions, we remain as sick as our secrets. Sharing them with just one other person is simply a collusion rather than a genuine sharing and an open acknowledgement of what our addictive disease has done to us and what we in turn have done to other people. The process of digging out and getting rid of shame needs, as the Big Book of Alcoholics Anonymous says about working the Twelve Steps, to be "fearless and thorough from the very start".

4. We need to see ourselves reflected in the mirror of the group and we need to acknowledge what we have in common with other members of the group. That way we can share our experience, strength and hope with each other and learn to feed each other with spiritual sustenance rather than starve alone.

5. Dumping our woes and tribulations in a one-to-one session, or even in a group of any kind, never helped anybody. Recovery comes from taking our minds off ourselves and reaching out to help others, rather than from continuing to be self-obsessed and self-pitying. So life is hard. So what? Active listening is much more healing than any amount of talking. The more people we listen to, the broader our perspectives and the more we are likely to learn. Craving to be heard is mere childish self-indulgence.

6. The "quick fixes" of passive therapies (anything that does not involve the active work of the patient) are a disaster. Getting up off our backsides and into meetings of the Anonymous Fellowships is the best thing we can ever do for ourselves and it is the best advice that can ever be given by a counsellor.

7. The sicker the counsellor, the sicker his or her concepts of recovery and the greater his or her popularity. Addictive disease flocks to where it feels safe. It is only when we listen to what we don't want to hear that we begin to get better.

8. Counsellors and Anonymous Fellowship sponsors alike should be judged on the same criteria. Are they following the recovery programme and working the Twelve Steps themselves? Where is the evidence of that in their personal and professional lives and in their relationships? Do they have something we want in our recovery? If not, run away - fast.

Addicts and Doctors

1. Doctors should be used for what they are good at. We need to consult them for physical and psychiatric illnesses and follow their advice. However, addicts themselves tend to know more about addictive disease as such, and how to treat it,

than doctors do. In fact many doctors do not even believe in its existence so this somewhat precludes them from knowing what to do about it.

2. Medical students are chosen primarily for their scientific aptitude, not for their emotional sensitivity nor for the variety and depth of their human experience. Yet these are equally important in the work that they eventually do as doctors. Addicts, most of all, need doctors with all these skills but tend to receive only science, particularly pharmacology.

3. Doctors expect patients to follow sensible advice. Addicts can't (not won't). That's the nature of the problem.

4. Doctors tend to analyse conditions and look for causes: antecedent causes (origins), contributory causes (complicating factors in life), and precipitant causes (the final immediate influence). The antecedent cause of addictive disease is probably genetic and other causes are largely irrelevant, however strongly both doctors and addicts - and other people - may hope and believe and even protest to the contrary.

5. Whoever coined the phrase " helping professions" did doctors and their patients grave damage. Clinical disaster occurs when doctors believe that they are helping but do not observe what is actually happening to their patients. In this specific respect, the history of medical treatment for addiction is a continuing catastrophe.

6. Doctors often have an image of "real" diseases that are worthy of their time and skill. Addiction tends not to qualify, even though addiction of one kind or another (particularly to alcohol, sugar and nicotine) often contributes significantly to major "real" diseases, such as cancer, heart attacks and strokes.

7. Doctors tend to prescribe. Some say it is because they do not have time to do otherwise. Others acknowledge that, for addicts, they would not know what else to do.

8. Doctors rarely understand the addictive nature of all mood-altering substances, including prescription medication such as pain-killers, tranquillisers, sleeping tablets and anti-depressants. In particular, they tend to look for specific physiological effects of withdrawal, cravings or tolerance rather than simply observe whether addicts use these substances to suppress feelings and avoid taking responsibility for their own behaviour.

9. Doctors tend to be reluctant to accept that some people are addictive by nature, while others are not. This can be seen straightforwardly in the observation that some people can use alcohol appropriately while others can't. The same principle applies to the capacity to use any mood-altering drug without progressing to dependence.

10. Doctors tend to specialise in "passive therapy", be it medical, surgical, physical or even "alternative", in which something is done to or for the patients. What addicts

need is the "active therapy" of the Twelve Step programme in which they are actively involved in working for their own recovery. "Passive therapy" may even get in the way of that.

Depression

1. The inner emptiness of addictive disease is often misdiagnosed as depressive illness. The former is common, the latter exceedingly rare, yet they tend to be diagnosed in inverse frequency.

2. The inner emptiness and spiritual loneliness of addictive disease drives sufferers towards the use of mood-altering substances (including mood-altering prescription medications), processes and relationships. These "treatments" wear off and therefore have to be taken again if the effect is to be maintained. In time, an increasing dose, with increasing frequency, may be necessary to provide the same effect as previously. Discontinuing the use may sometimes result in immediate withdrawal symptoms but always results in return to the original sense of inner emptiness unless an alternative outlet is found.

3. "Reactive" depression (best termed "unhappiness") is the term used when the sadness follows a specific event. This is a normal human experience and requires no medicinal treatment whatever. The patients should be comforted, supported and encouraged to use their own resources. Medication impedes the normal physiological process of grieving.

4. "Endogenous" depression (from within), when there is no sign of any form of addictive behaviour, is rare. It is probably a genetically-inherited chemical imbalance, but is sometimes induced by illness or by hormonal changes. It has to be diagnosed by exclusion, first ruling out the possibility of addictive disease, looking at all possible outlets of addictive or compulsive behaviour. True endogenous depression could theoretically be treated appropriately with anti-depressants. However, this risks creating, in any patient but especially in addicts, the saddest of all doctor-induced disorders: self-justifying zombies, suppressing all their feelings (not simply the bad ones) and living in thrall to the pharmaceutical industry.

5. "Manic depression" is a specific clinical condition, quite distinct from any other form of depression. It has to be distinguished from normal mood swings that can happen in anyone, but particularly in addicts. Indeed, addicts - commonly alcoholics - are sometimes misdiagnosed as suffering from manic depression simply because of the fluctuations in their mood.

6. "Clinical depression" is a term used to justify the prescription of mood-altering drugs. Most commonly it is used (with the addicts' connivance) to avoid diagnosing addictive disease as such. Perhaps the term is felt to be less pejorative than "addiction". Further rationalisation, for example saying that anti-depressants

simply "put the brain in a splint for a time so that problems can be solved with a clear head", is the opposite of the truth: they compound the problem with a prescription drug addiction - and withdrawal from this dependency can be exceedingly difficult.

7.   There are many things that happen in the lives of addicts that lead us to "choose to depress": we may not perceive an alternative method of reacting to circumstance or communicating our feelings to others. The Twelve Step programme helps us to accept normal turns of fate, to develop a sense of responsibility for our own thoughts, feelings, actions and reactions, to take our minds off ourselves by reaching out to help others, and hence make "depression" a thing of the past.

Alcoholism

1.   Alcohol leads to one hundred deaths per day in the U.K. and three hundred in the U.S.A.

One in five of all hospital beds is occupied by a person with an alcohol-related condition.

One in two of all people seen in accident and emergency departments are there as a result of the use of alcohol or drugs, either by the sufferer or by other people.

The number of days lost from work and the amount of damage done to industry, through alcohol is far greater than from any other cause, including illness, accidents and strikes.

2.   Alcoholism is not caused by drinking too much alcohol. Alcohol is one of many "treatments" for the inner emptiness of addictive disease. The term "alcoholism" is a misnomer. It names the illness after one of its treatments. It would be like calling a sore throat "Penicillinism". Alcohol is an inappropriate treatment because of the damage it causes. Alcoholics Anonymous (A.A.) is the more appropriate treatment.

3.   Most of the population can drink perfectly sensibly and merely need to be reminded not to drink and drive or do other potentially dangerous activities while under the influence of alcohol.

4.   An alcoholic cannot predict what will happen to his or her alcohol consumption after the first use of alcohol in any day. It is therefore the first drink that does the damage. No alcoholic can ever be taught to drink sensibly: abstinence is the only effective treatment, coupled with regular attendance at meetings of A.A. in order to prevent relapse.

5.   Addicts who use alcohol are not identified by the quantity they drink, nor by the time of day they drink, nor by what particular drink they consume. They are identified by addictive behavioural characteristics - by why they drink - and by the damaging consequences from the effect of alcohol on various aspects of their lives.

6. Alcohol acts as both a stimulant and a tranquilliser and is commonly used in conjunction with other drugs. Withdrawal effects can be severe and can include epileptic fits, against which the patient needs to be protected medicinally.

7. Putting down alcohol and instead using nicotine or food simply removes the specific consequences of drinking alcohol: it does not affect addictive disease as such and therefore it leaves the inner sense of emptiness. In this "dry drunk" state the behaviour towards other people may be just as bad as before.

8. An appropriate diagnostic test is to see whether someone can remain totally abstinent for the rest of each day (and without tempers flaring or spirits dropping) after having two drinks at lunch-time on each of seven successive days. In this way, addictive disease can be diagnosed and treated appropriately many years before it wreaks havoc in every aspect of the sufferer's life.

9. PROMIS treats "alcoholism" alongside all other addictions so that patients come to understand the true nature of their problem with addictive behaviour as something that goes with them rather than merely with a specific substance.

Cannabis

1. Alcohol and cannabis are similar in three respects: they are used for social pleasure because of their capacity to alter the mood, they have some medicinal properties, and they are addictive to those people who suffer from addictive disease.
One significant difference is that the use and sale of alcohol is legal but of cannabis is illegal. Another is that the excessive use of alcohol often leads to violence.

2. If cannabis were to be legalised then there would probably be little further interest in its medicinal properties. The various claims for its medicinal value are rarely anything special. The pharmacopoeia already abounds with alternatives that are mostly highly effective. The publication of a book such as *Marihuana the Forbidden Medicine* (Lester Grinspoon MD and James B Bakalar: Yale University Press) would be very unlikely on economic grounds if cannabis were legal and available in shops rather than on prescription. For example, what sale would there be for a book on the medicinal effects of alcohol? They certainly exist in anaesthesia and antisepsis but who cares now that we can all drink it anyway? This particular book on the medicinal properties of cannabis cites relief from nausea, pain and muscle spasms and claims that it alleviates symptoms of glaucoma, multiple sclerosis, AIDS, migraine and other debilitating ailments. The authors claim that cannabis is "a remarkably safe substance".

3. By contrast *The Great Brain Robbery* (Tom Scott and Trevor Grice: Aurora Press 1998) emphasizes the damage that cannabis does in particular to the capacity of the brain for memory and motivation. Perhaps those who do not value their minds have no need to worry.

4. In fact both books are right: cannabis does have medicinal properties and it also has the capacity to cause considerable damage. Exactly the same is true for alcohol and also for many pharmaceutical substances. Yet the only popular book to sing the praises of a pharmaceutical drug is *Listening to Prozac* (Peter D Kramer: Fourth Estate) and the reason for its popularity is that the drug enables people to avoid responsibility for their own feelings. This is exactly what Prozac has in common with alcohol and cannabis and other mood-altering substances. They provide an easy way out - at a price.

5. The legalisation, or decriminalisation, of cannabis has become a *cause celebre*. Granted the law is inconsistent in its treatment, on the one hand, of nicotine, sugar and alcohol and, on the other hand, of the various substances, including cannabis, that are currently illegal. Granted that nicotine, sugar and alcohol each cause many more deaths than all the illegal drugs put together. Yet the hullabaloo on behalf of cannabis is more a battle between generations or cultures than one based on legal or clinical principles. "You've got your drug; I want mine" is really what is behind it all.

6. Cannabis is a major addictive drug to some people. Divisions between "hard" and "soft" drugs are artificial. The only important feature of any potentially addictive drug is whether, in some people, the first use in any day tends to trigger the next. That spells trouble and progressive destruction and that is exactly the same for alcohol and cannabis and other mood-altering substances. If you are among those people, you are quite likely to be in the forefront of those interested in the medicinal properties of cannabis and in its legalisation. But beware; you are the very people most likely to be damaged by it.

Recreational Drug Addiction

1. Not all users of recreational (street) drugs are addicted to them, any more than all users of alcohol are alcoholics. However, the defect in perception that is the basic flaw in addictive disease leads addicts themselves to be the last people to believe that they really do have an addiction problem.

2. Eventually addicts seek help when the pain of continuing as they are is perceived to be greater than the pain of giving up. Therefore anything that reduces the painful consequences of addiction (paying off the dealers, providing lawyers, covering the general costs of living, prescribing alternative drugs) simply prolongs the addiction and makes the risks of even greater damage, and possible death, more rather than less likely. The therapeutic challenge, in this as in other forms of addiction, is therefore to try to persuade personal and professional helpers to let the addicts suffer the consequences of their behaviour.

3. Any drug that has a mood-altering effect can be used addictively. There is therefore no difference between soft and hard drugs other than (mostly) in the length of time it takes to be significantly damaged by their use.

4. Contrary to popular belief and the common protests of addicts, detoxification is usually the most simple and straightforward aspect of treatment. Learning how to stay off drugs is much more difficult. Heroin is detoxified on Methadone on a reducing basis over four to eight days at the most. Tranquillisers, sleeping tablets and anti-depressants have to be detoxified much more slowly, over a period of at least two to three weeks. Cocaine and crack, amphetamines (speed), LSD (acid), Ecstasy and cannabis require no detoxification, although mild night sedation may be helpful for the first two or three nights. A major advantage of employing former addicts in Minnesota Method treatment centres as counselling staff is that new patients cannot deceive former patients on how much detoxification they need.

5. New patients should be introduced to group therapy as soon as they are able to walk. Hopefully, by the time detoxification is coming to an end (the most likely time for patients to discharge themselves from treatment), there will be an established bond of understanding and encouragement between the patients.

6. The concept of "harm minimisation" and the practice of "needle exchange schemes" are the complete antithesis of recovery. Addicts should be encouraged to become totally drug-free. Anything less is unethical: it offers less than the best option to the patients, sometimes because of fear of damage to society rather than out of genuine concern for the patients. Talk of the potential risk of AIDS or hepatitis, or of the opportunities to have a settled life on a regularly prescribed maintenance dose of a pharmaceutic drug, such as Methadone or various anti-depressants, simply perpetuates the disease with all its risks. Furthermore, addicts commonly sell or augment their prescribed medications.

7. Even at best, the life available on prescribed drugs is a life devoid of genuine feeling. Is that what we would tolerate for our own loved ones? If not, we should never allow mood-altering prescribed drugs of this nature to be given (under whatever rationalisation) to addicts.

8. Addicts commonly want to blame their childhood experiences and current social circumstances for their addiction. These may influence the specific addictive outlets that any particular addict may use, but the basic addictive nature is probably genetically inherited. Thus the prime purpose of Minnesota Method treatment is to give sufferers an understanding of the nature of addictive disease and what needs to be done to keep it in remission on a continuing daily basis for the rest of their lives. Quick fixes of any kind don't work. Following the Twelve Step programme of Narcotics Anonymous does work - and provides a drug-free life that enables recovering addicts to create happy and fulfilling relationships, develop their own personalities, and follow their own hopes and ambitions in life.

Prescription Drug Addiction

1. Prescription drug addiction is the most difficult of all addictions to treat. It shares with anorexia the sheer difficulty of detoxification. It shares with nicotine addiction the belief that it isn't really a major problem and even that it is necessary for emotional survival. Additionally, prescription drug addiction has the cast-iron justification that the drugs are provided by doctors. Nevertheless, prescription drug addiction comes about not simply as a result of irresponsible prescribing but also from the individual's own addictive nature.

2. Addiction to prescription drugs comes in two distinct forms:

    i. Poly-drug addiction in which prescription drugs are used alongside other drugs. Thus, stimulants ("uppers") and tranquillisers and sleeping tablets ("downers") are used together with alcohol, cannabis, hallucinogens, cocaine, heroin and other drugs in order to vary their effects, Anti-depressants are used addictively, partly through the misdiagnosis (by doctor and patient alike) of "depression" instead of acknowledging the inner emptiness of addictive disease, partly to suppress the emotional consequences of addictive behaviour, and partly in a determined attempt to prove to self and others that the real cause of all the problems is in the environment or in a medical condition rather than in the addict and his or her addictive behaviour;

    ii. Primary prescription drug addiction, in which this is the sole or dominant addiction. These sufferers commonly take the same dose of tranquilliser, sleeping tablet or anti-depressant for many years, far beyond the time of influence of the event that triggered the initial prescription. Doctor and patient collude in a bizarre concept of "help": the zombie thanks the pusher. Withdrawal symptoms are used to reaffirm the "need" for more drugs.

3. Poly-drug users can be safely detoxified from even enormous quantities of prescription drugs in three to four weeks. Primary prescription drug addiction takes much longer, preferably three months, reducing the dosage by one twelfth each successive week. This has obvious financial implications if detoxification is done on an in-patient basis (there is also considerable discouragement as other patients pass through treatment much faster). Outpatient detoxification has obvious problems in supervision.

4. All addicts have to beware of the mood-altering properties of some prescription drugs. There are significant risks of relapse when using pain-killers, tranquillisers, anti-depressants and sleeping tablets. Less obvious is the alcohol base of many syrups and the mood-altering properties of anti-histamines and even some medications for peptic ulcers. Addicts know perfectly well when a substance has a mood-altering effect and we have to develop a sense of responsibility for our recovery in not using those medications, especially when doctors may commonly be ignorant of the nature of addictive disease and the risks of any mood-altering medications.

5. Some psychotropic medications, such as anti-psychotics for schizophrenia and Lithium for genuine manic depression (as opposed to the mood swings of alcoholism falsely diagnosed as being due to manic depression), are necessary for these specific clinical conditions. These medications are not mood-altering and therefore have no effect on addictive disease.

6. Mood-altering prescription medications should never be stopped abruptly. Withdrawal effects can be exceedingly severe and suicide can be a significant risk.

7. The most important strategy for prescription drug addiction is prevention: doctors should not prescribe these drugs in the first place other than in exceptional circumstances. Genuine depressive illness is rare. There are generally better ways of treating emotional problems than through pharmaceutical substances and there are few things more dangerous to addicts than giving them prescription drugs that aggravate or perpetuate their illness.

Nicotine Addiction

1. Nicotine addiction is the most severe and destructive of all addictions. In the UK it is responsible for three hundred deaths a day (one thousand in the U.S.A.), whereas all the illegal drugs together in the U.K. kill only five. Yet nicotine, in the form of cigarettes, is not only legal but widely considered to be a normal or even necessary part of personal and social life.

2. Patients rarely request treatment for nicotine addiction as such. More commonly, patients in treatment for other addictions say that they are not prepared to give up smoking. Usually they say that they have to have some "pleasures" in life. They do not consider cigarette smoking to be an important addiction in their current lives. They may even have been advised by professional counsellors and by people in the Anonymous Fellowships that they should not give up everything at once. PROMIS considers that all these attitudes are misguided and we do everything we can to encourage patients to give up smoking while under our care and supported by the rest of the group of patients.

3. We know from previous experience that insisting that patients give up smoking may simply cause them to walk immediately out of treatment. That helps nobody.

4. All PROMIS counselling staff are non-smokers. We do not consider smokers to be drug-free and therefore we do not consider them to be capable of doing counselling work. They would be using chemicals to suppress their feelings and could not therefore expect patients to do otherwise.

5. Cigarette smokers have a much higher rate of relapse back to other addictions than non-smokers. The PROMIS belief is that any continuing addiction is a major risk to recovery. It is for this specific reason that we emphasise the importance for addicts

of all kinds to give up smoking.

6. PROMIS does not recommend the use of nicotine chewing gum or patches as we believe that these are unnecessary. Going "cold turkey" is often not as difficult as imagined. However, gradual reduction over one week, giving up first the "unnecessary" cigarettes (such as the second one immediately after the first) and then the "automatic" cigarettes (such as with a cup of coffee or when on the telephone) and then finally going "cold-turkey", works well enough. Furthermore, gums or patches containing nicotine are themselves addictive and are therefore often used by addicts as a substitute addiction rather than simply for a short process of detoxification.

7. PROMIS does everything we can to bring to the notice of a wider audience the similarity between nicotine addiction and other forms of addiction and hence the importance of recognising the inadequacy of "quick-fix" treatments that merely help people to stop smoking at a particular time rather than stay off for ever. PROMIS emphasises the need for an appropriate diagnostic process looking specifically for an addictive tendency, as opposed to casual or habitual use, and for addicts we use the Twelve Step therapeutic approach to deal with nicotine addiction right at the start rather than focusing on general educational programmes that don't work or relying on heroic medical treatments after the physical damage has already been done.

Eating Disorders

1. Eating disorders are not primarily anything to do with food or body weight. As with any other compulsion, they are primarily concerned with our determination to control feelings. Bingeing, starving, vomiting, purging and the use of mood-altering food substances are what many sufferers from addictive disease have discovered to be effective.

2. Refining sugar and flour removes the fibre content, thereby causing immense problems in the physical health of the general population, particularly in the gastro-intestinal and cardiovascular systems. For those with eating disorders there is the further complication that sugar and white flour are, for us, addictive drugs that have a particular mood-altering effect.

3. Common cross-addictions with eating disorders are shopping and spending (and shoplifting when money runs out), overworking and under- or over-exercising.

4. Anorexia, bulimia and compulsive overeating are not separate conditions: they are merely different aspects of the same underlying condition. Some sufferers get stuck in one particular behaviour but many will use different eating disorder behaviours at different times of life. Although feeding an anorexic patient may be a medically necessary initial process (as with detoxification for alcoholism or drug-addiction),

focusing on the food itself, or on physical appearance and body weight, does nothing whatever in the long term to heal the mood disorder.

5. Commonly, doctors prescribe anti-depressants to "treat" eating disorders. They work in the same way that heroin would work for toothache. They smother the symptoms temporarily, fail to deal with the underlying problem, and may result in a secondary addiction that is very difficult to treat.

6. Eating disorders do not develop as a result of abuse or abandonment or other problems in childhood or from social or environmental problems in later life. Anorexia is not a dieting regime that has gone too far, nor a result of influence by the fashion industry. The disturbance of body image and the poor self-worth are part of the basic clinical condition rather than a reaction to anything else. Correspondingly, over-exercising is not primarily a consequence of trying to get fit, nor is overworking a consequence of trying to produce: they are all attempts to control inner feelings by changing external factors of one kind or another. Even self-harming, a common occurrence in sufferers from eating disorders, is primarily an attempt to control feelings.

7. There is nothing "special and different" in treating eating disorders. Alcoholics have to drink to stay alive, just as sufferers from eating disorders have to eat to stay alive, but they avoid drinks that have mood-altering effects. Similarly, sufferers from eating disorders have to avoid sugar and white flour but can eat anything else and must develop normal healthy eating patterns. Some foods that become particular "binge" foods should initially be avoided but can usually be reintroduced safely later on. Learning to have three regular, nourishing, well-balanced meals each day (and nothing in between: no snacks whatever) is a necessary part of retraining for normality.

8. Eating disorders have nothing to do with food allergies, vitamin and trace-element deficiencies, intestinal candidiasis, M.E. or other conditions that may have some clinical basis in some people but which are more commonly part of the spectrum of obsessional behaviour seen in people who try to control their feelings and avoid facing up to the realities of life.

9. The consequences of eating disorders can be as disastrous, medically and socially, as any other addictive behaviour. Equally, they can be treated successfully in just the same way through a Twelve Step programme in an appropriate Anonymous Fellowship.

Behavioural Addictions

1. There is nothing particularly difficult in putting down a behavioural addiction, as opposed to an addictive substance. Any addict knows perfectly well when he or she is using a particular behaviour addictively, for its "buzz" or mood-altering effect rather than for the purpose that anyone else would use it. The difficulty is in persuading ourselves that we need to put it down - but that is the same for any addiction.

2. It is just as important for addicts to put down our behavioural addictions as it is for us to put down our addictive substances. There is no such thing as a "healthy" or "positive" addiction. All addictive behaviour is progressive and destructive. All addictive behaviour corrupts normal behaviour, taking away its pleasures and benefits. Furthermore, behavioural addictions keep our addictive disease "ticking over", and it is only a matter of time before a stressful event leads us to clamour for "the real thing" and hence return to a substance addiction.

3. Each behavioural addiction has to be examined specifically for its addictive component. We cannot give up the behaviour altogether (it is part of normal life) but we can give up the aspects of that behaviour that are addictive and which we use specifically for mood-altering effect.

    i.   We all take risks every day but only compulsive gamblers and risk-takers take risks for the sake of the risk itself.

    ii. We all need to work to achieve results and to earn money but only workaholics work in order to fill up time and to make ourselves feel better about ourselves.

    iii. We all need to shop and spend, and in some extreme circumstances we might even steal, but we generally do so in order to obtain specific things that we need or want, whereas the compulsive shopper, spender or thief gets a mood-altering effect from the process itself.

    iv. We should all take exercise to keep fit, whereas the exercise addict craves perfection in performance or appearance and hence in self-image.

    v.   Sex and love are the most tender things that we can ever share with another human being, but for a sex and love addict they are merely commodities, interchangeable with any mood-altering substance, process or relationship.

4. All addictive outlets have a behavioural component. It is important to acknowledge this when confronting the full requirements of abstinence. Nicotine addiction gives us something to do with our hands and mouths and helps us to open conversations and to share things with others. Alcohol may help to provide convivial environments and reduce inhibitions. Bingeing, purging, vomiting and starving are mood-altering processes in their own right, irrespective of the mood-altering properties of sugar and refined carbohydrates. Recreational drugs have a "junkie

culture" all of their own. Each and every addiction has a whole constellation of accompanying behaviour that has to be replaced with something equally supportive but more positive. Working the Twelve Steps of the Anonymous Fellowships is the positive creative behaviour that counters the mood disturbance that leads to addictive behaviour of all kinds.

Sex

1. Sex is an activity of the mind, expressed by the body. If the mind has no respect for itself, no principles or values that are worth having, then the body will survive for a time on purely animal instinct but will later surely fail. When the body is blamed - and pathetic measures taken to stimulate its performance - the finger is pointing in the wrong direction: it is most commonly the head and heart that are at fault.

2. The use of alcohol and recreational drugs may initially reduce inhibitions and give increased sexual stimulation. However, this is at the expense of longer-term physical dependence upon these substances for sexual gratification. Furthermore, they damage the capacity to create a genuine relationship with a partner.

3. Alcohol stimulates the production of sex hormone binding globulin (S.H.B.G.) in the liver. This inactivates the sex hormones, leading to various physical consequences and the failure of sex drive.

4. Sexual orientation is probably genetically inherited. Promiscuity, in the form of sex and love addiction rather than simple opportunism or lack of deeper values, may also be genetically inherited. Sexual orientation cannot be influenced by a Twelve Step programme or anything else: it is the way some people are made and that's that. Sex and love addiction, however, be it homosexual or heterosexual, involves behaviour and can therefore be influenced, most appropriately on a continuing daily basis through a Twelve Step programme. We cannot change the fact that we are addicts but we can put our active addiction into remission and respect our inter-relationships with other people.

5. Seeking instant gratification is a characteristic of any addiction. Demanding it (in subtle or very unsubtle ways) from other people, without any true consideration for them, is also a characteristic of any addiction. When this takes the form of sexual gratification, the spiritual degradation is total. The most tender, beautiful and vigorous expression of love for another human being becomes debased as just another mood-altering experience, no more valuable or personal than a glass of whisky or shot of heroin.

6. The challenge of developing just one sexual relationship, so that it becomes continuingly exhilarating and inventive, begins with developing an interpersonal relationship with exactly those features. Mere physical attraction, in the absence of spiritual attraction, cannot survive the harsh light of reality. A truly loving

relationship is strengthened by physical attraction and is rewarded with sexual passion indefinitely.

7.   Fabulous sex is one of the great benefits of recovery. Imagine having sex with someone with whom you have built a truly loving relationship: the prize of recovery is eternal youth!

Communication

1.   Relationships in recovery should theoretically be no different from other, non-addicted, people's relationships. However, in this particular respect addicts have a considerable advantage. Few people ever do as much work on themselves as addicts have to do in order to get into recovery, few people develop such understanding and acceptance of other people's behaviour, and few people are able to accept the trials and tribulations of life with such equanimity as those who work a Twelve Step programme on a daily basis. The prospect for deeply fulfilling and rewarding relationships in recovery is set fair.

2.   Learning to communicate effectively is very rewarding. So often when people say "We do not communicate", what they really mean is "She won't do as I say" or "He doesn't see it my way". There is no chance of effective communication if we expect the other person to make all the allowances, considerations and changes. Primarily we need to examine what we put out (verbally and non-verbally) and how we receive. By being more perceptive of our own skills (or lack of them) we make ourselves more available to others: our own lives become richer even if other people make no change whatever.

3.   We each have "filters" that determine what we know or otherwise receive. Our childhood experiences, education, current preoccupations and many other filters result in our hearing or perceiving things in a particular way. The same is true for other people. If we are unaware of our own filters, let alone of theirs, we run the risk of feeling permanently misunderstood - and that would be our own fault for being so insensitive. Communication depends on what arrives as much as on what is put out and it is up to us to ensure that we are aware of that.

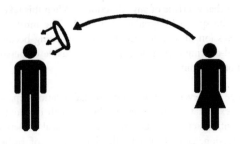

a new life healing depression

4. Our "open" door (the route through which we are most accessible), our "target" door (towards which we need to be guided) and our "trap" door (through which other people will disappear without trace or hope of any effective communication) vary from one person to another. Characteristically the doors of addicts and compulsive helpers are as follows:

	Addict	Helper
Open Door	Feelings	Thoughts
Trap Door	Thoughts	Actions
Target Door	Actions	Feelings

Thus, addicts need to change their behaviour but are most accessible through their feelings rather than their thoughts, which can descend merely into intellectualisation and argumentativeness. Conversely, compulsive helpers will respond favourably to reason but will tend to avoid acknowledging their true feelings by being eternally busy. There is no right or wrong in these or other forms of characteristic make-up. We simply need to know our own make-up and that of other people, particularly our nearest and dearest, if we are to communicate effectively.

Addictive Relationships

1. "Co-dependency" means so many different things to different people that it means nothing at all. Further, the idea that parents, through deliberately or unwittingly abusing or abandoning their children, cause them to become "co-dependent", whence they subsequently become addicted, is dangerous nonsense. Firstly, there are many people who have been abused and abandoned who never become addicted. Secondly, and even more importantly, addicts at any stage of recovery, but particularly in the early years, need to take their own inventories rather than their parents' or other people's. When therapists, and even Anonymous Fellowships, take other people's inventories (even while purporting to do otherwise) they may be hugely popular - for obvious reasons - but they cause immense damage and should be given a wide berth .

2. A primary relationship addict, who uses other people as if they were drugs, should be differentiated from a compulsive helper, who uses himself or herself as a drug for other people. The addict and the compulsive helper may have a fatal attraction for each other, being locked into each other's addictive behaviour in a dreadful dance. Furthermore, if one particular relationship breaks up, either partner will soon find a replacement with the same or comparable addictive tendencies as the last. In this one sense they could justifiably be said to be co-dependent.

3. When two primary addicts (not compulsive helpers) are in a relationship together, the early stages of recovery of one can be exceedingly difficult if not synchronised with the other. The pull of addictive disease is always stronger than the pull of recovery so the risk of relapse is considerable. For this reason the addict who is

newly recovering needs considerable support in the Anonymous Fellowships and needs to be aware of the significant risks of trying to do what he or she often most wants to do: to get some special person into recovery. At this time, in addition to attending his or her primary Fellowship, it would be sensible to attend Helpers Anonymous or an equivalent "family" Fellowship.

4. It is dangerous to make new relationships in early recovery (the first year or even two) because each addict tends to be attracted to others at his or her own level of recovery. Thus, when addicts walk out of treatment, they often do so in pairs, being attracted both physically and mentally to the bizarre wreckage in each other. New relationships are almost bound to falter when one partner grows ahead of the other in terms of recovery and spiritual health: the disease becomes progressively less attractive. Yet again, it is more probable that the disease will have the stronger pull and will undermine the recovery of the other.

5. 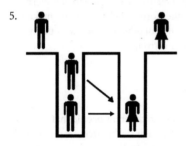 It is best to wait for new relationships until one's own recovery is on firm ground. As attitudes and values change with increasing recovery, so the nature of new relationships inevitably changes. When recovery is secure the new relationship should also be secure because the mutual attraction will be based on positive values and attitudes. When we have climbed out of the pit, our horizons are infinite. Indeed, major indications of our level of recovery are the quality of our personal and professional relationships and our capacity to accept that, after causing so much damage over the years, we can afford to take an equivalent amount (up to that level and no more) in return.

Compulsive Helping

1. Compulsive helping is far more than just manipulative "people-pleasing". It is a progressive and destructive addictive behaviour in its own right. It is, however, the "mirror image" of other addictions. Whereas a primary addict uses addictive substances, behaviours and relationships in order to be "fixed", even using other people as if they were drugs, the compulsive helper needs to be needed and uses himself or herself as a drug for other people.

2. Inevitably, addicts and compulsive helpers tend to form relationships together. Addicts do not cause people to become compulsive helpers: they were probably born that way through genetic inheritance comparable to that of the addicts. However, compulsive helpers tend to stay with addicts - and even go looking for them - whereas other, healthier, people tend to leave. Thus, not everyone in an addictive family will necessarily be an addict or a compulsive helper. However, addicts and compulsive helpers tend to stay locked in a relationship together and often marry

each other and have children, thus keeping the limited gene pool (probably about ten per cent of the population) ticking over.

3. Compulsive helping is not a "nice" behaviour, nor is it actually helpful. It tends to be arrogant and patronising in the belief that "nanny knows best" and it takes away the opportunity for other people to learn from their own painful experiences. The compulsive helper gets the pain, and feels virtuous while wallowing in it, and is oblivious of the damage that the "helping" has caused. Addicts need to be confronted and given the full consequences of their behaviour if they are ever to change. Compulsive helpers, by perpetually bailing them out, enable them to stay as they are. As the addict progressively deteriorates, getting more and more hooked into the addiction, the compulsive helper sees this as an opportunity to be needed even more. Eventually they both crack up, each destroyed by their own and each other's addictive behaviour.

4. Some people are both addicts and compulsive helpers, tending to be the one in some relationships and the other in others. This is not as complex as it sounds, once we work out which 'hat' we tend to have on in each of our relationships.

5. The addictive behaviours of compulsive helping are caretaking (when caring goes too far and becomes a hindrance) and self-denial (when the pain we are prepared to tolerate becomes increasingly destructive). These addictive behaviours exactly correspond to the blame and self-pity that are the fundamental behavioural characteristics of primary addicts.

6. The dividing line between normal helping and compulsive helping is crossed when the compulsive helper needs to be needed and then justifies the behaviour, just as the primary addict justifies his or hers. To do something helpful is fine - and compulsive helpers can do something genuinely helpful - but why did we do it? To be kind and creative or, alternatively, to feel that we ourselves are something special? The former is a virtue, the latter a vice.

7. Compulsive helpers, for obvious reasons, often join the "helping" professions where they burn themselves out on the altar of self-righteousness, ultimately becoming resentful of their patients, pupils or other charges and neglectful of their true responsibilities.

8. The natural tendency for compulsive helpers is to want to reach out to help addicts. Recovery comes in Helpers Anonymous when they reach out to help other compulsive helpers.

Tough Love

1. Tough Love is the capacity to love the individual while confronting the disease and making the sufferer fully responsible for the consequences of all his or her actions.

2. Tough love should have equal emphasis on both words. Further, the toughness applies as much to the family member as to the primary sufferer. Tough love hurts the family member

    i. because it involves allowing the primary sufferer, whom he or she loves, to experience the full painful consequences of addictive disease

    ii. because it may involve the family member in resisting his or her own addictive urges to "fix" all the problems by taking over the management of the life of the primary sufferer.

3. Tough love should be kind, gentle and understanding to both the family member and the primary sufferer, while nonetheless allowing each to be fully responsible for his or her own feelings and behaviour.

4. Sometimes a family member will believe that tough love involves refusal to help the sufferer to seek recovery, for example by refusing to pay for specific Twelve Step programme counselling or in-patient treatment. This is simply "black belt Al Anon" behaviour: hoping to repay the primary sufferer for all the pain felt by the family member.

    Further, a family member may find it difficult to "let go" of the primary sufferer while he or she is in treatment and may still want to find out everything that goes on in a treatment centre on a day-to-day basis and thereby continue to "fix" by proxy. Tough love requires that the family member "lets go" of the primary sufferer and seeks help for himself or herself through an appropriate Family Fellowship, concentrating primarily on his or her own recovery from the addictive urge to fix or control the lives of others.

5. Tough love by the family member is, more than anything else, what tends to bring the primary sufferer to seek his or her own recovery. However, it may fail even then, and it should be emphasised that family members benefit for their own sake from involvement in the Family Fellowships regardless of what may happen to the primary sufferer. We learn to love even while rejecting and confronting addictive behaviour. That may be tough but we can live with it.

Examples of Tough Love

In Alcoholism:

Not clearing up physical messes caused by the primary sufferer.
Not apologising to other people for the behaviour of the primary sufferer.

Not telling lies to the employer, the courts or anyone else.

Not paying off the debts of the primary sufferer.
Not putting up bail or hiring lawyers to defend the sufferer in any alcohol-related case.
Not allowing yourself or your children to be passengers in a car if the driver is the primary sufferer and he or she has been drinking.

Not altering your own social life and neglecting your own friendships as the result of the behaviour of the primary sufferer.

Not taking on more work yourself in order to take over financial responsibility from the primary sufferer while he or she continues to drink.

Not going along with diagnoses of "depression" or "stress".

Not allowing children to suffer in any way. First of all do whatever is necessary to protect the children. The relationship between parents or other adults can be restored (if so wished) after the primary sufferer is in recovery.

Not doubting your own sanity or believing that the problems are all your own fault.

In Drug Addiction:

Not allowing any illegal drugs in your own home: threaten to call the police if you do find drugs or have significant reasons to suspect their use. All threats must be carried out. Give no second chances and accept no "explanations".

To adults, and in children old enough to be independent, offer a straight choice: drugs or home - and stick to it.

Not paying fines, putting up bail or finding lawyers for any drug-related offences.

Not providing money to pay debts to dealers or anyone else, regardless of threats, or even to buy "essentials". Any money given will almost certainly be spent directly on drugs. Gifts will most probably either be sold or will enable any other available money to be spent on drugs. Gifts should be only what any "normal" friend or family member would provide.

Not obtaining addictive drugs or collecting prescriptions for mood-altering medications on behalf of the sufferer for any reason, even in order to ensure the personal safety of the sufferer or the purity of the drugs.

Reporting all thefts to the police.

In Eating Disorders:

Not involving yourself at all in anything whatever to do with how or when or how little or how much the primary sufferer eats.

Not allowing the primary sufferer to be involved in food preparation as a smoke screen that hides the eating behaviour.

Not allowing any form of inappropriate behaviour.

Not providing special foods or special portions.

Not buying into the spurious diagnoses of food allergy, intestinal candidiasis, vitamin and trace element deficiencies and suchlike. The primary concern has to be the eating disorder itself.

In Compulsive Behaviour of any kind:

Not taking responsibility yourself for any consequences of the behaviour of the primary sufferer.

Not easing the burden of the consequences of addictive behaviour in any way.

Looking after your own needs.

In Compulsive Helping:

Not allowing the compulsive helper to take any form of responsibility that should rightly belong to the primary sufferer or to someone else.

Not allowing compulsive helpers to undermine appropriate tough love.

Not being taken in by the belief that "help" of one kind or another is always helpful: it may actually hinder someone else's growth towards maturity.

Genuine Help

1. Recognise that the sufferer from addictive disease (whether suffering from primary addiction or compulsive helping) is in the grip of a disease that controls much of his or her words and actions. Occasionally there will still be glimpses of the real person, pleading for help and desperately trying to be free, but then the alien disease, like a persistent parasite, takes hold again and for a time destroys everything in its path: all hope, all trust, all honesty, all love, all relationships. Then again comes a glimpse of the suffering individual: confused, frightened and lonely. Then the disease smashes in yet again, utterly arrogant in its demand for total control, determined to have all the answers in any discussion, determined to make everyone else feel helpless, frustrated, angry and isolated and to turn the words and actions of the sufferer to its own absolute advantage.

2. Avoid trying to reason with the disease. Stay quietly confident of your own knowledge of truth. Seek the help of Helpers Anonymous, Al Anon, Families Anonymous or other appropriate anonymous Family Groups in order to meet other people who have similar first-hand experience of the living hell of being at close quarters with the insanity of addictive disease. Learn from them to love the sufferer while still hating his or her disease. Learn from them the strength to risk saying no to the disease: to refuse to cover up, tidy up or pay up but to allow the sufferer to take the full consequences of the addiction. Be assured that the risks taken now would later on be even greater as the disease progresses. Learn from the Family Fellowships to allow your own sanity to redevelop by letting go of the self-imposed stranglehold of trying to be a "caretaker" for someone else.

3. Recognise that alcohol, cannabis, cocaine, Ecstasy, LSD, heroin, Methadone, pain-killers, tranquillisers, anti-depressants, sleeping tablets, caffeine, nicotine, sugar and white flour and other mood-altering substances are all cross-addictive to sufferers from addictive disease and that all these "drugs" feed the disease regardless of whether they are legal, illegal, medically prescribed or considered to be foods.

4. Recognise that there is no blame in being an addict, only in the choices of behaviour towards other people. As with short-sight, diabetes, epilepsy and many other diseases or conditions, it happens in some people but not in others. Addictive disease, as opposed to physiological addiction, is not a significant potential risk for everyone. Some people may suffer damaging consequences from just one use of an addictive substance or process. That does not mean that they are addicts. Other people may use an addictive substance or process regularly. That also does not necessarily mean that they are addicts. The determining factor in addiction is not what or when one uses but why one does so.

5. Recognise that addictive disease affects different people in different ways and is very variable in its intensity but that all sufferers share the "denial" of believing that they are not addicted: the crucial test of addiction is not whether one can stop the use of an addictive substance or behaviour but whether one can happily stay off and not be

drawn back to it or to something equally addictive.

6.	Recognise that although addictive disease is probably genetically inherited, and certainly runs in families, this does not mean that all parents or all children of sufferers from addictive disease will necessarily have addictive disease themselves.

7.	Learn to be things rather than do things for the sufferer. A true friend would not do anything that would enable the disease to continue but would instead take the difficult and risky path of confronting it, while still loving the sufferer, despite all the harshness that the disease will cause the sufferer to throw in return. The risk of confronting the disease may be the possible death of the sufferer; the risk of not doing so may be his or her almost certain death from the progression of the disease. These alternatives are stark and fearful - but realistic.

8.	Learn to differentiate between normal helping (doing what anyone else would do) and compulsive helping (taking excessive responsibility for someone else instead of being appropriately responsible to him or her). Compulsive helping actually reduces the recipient's capacity to learn from experience. Going to the opposite extreme and interpreting every pleasant or generous act as an instance of compulsive helping is just silly - but it is often done by critics who try to undermine the concept of compulsive helping so that they do not have to take full responsibility for their own thoughts, feelings, actions and reactions.

9.	Recognise in time, perhaps only from the despair of repeated failure, that you yourself did not cause the sufferer's addictive disease, cannot control it and cannot cure it. Recognise that in time you will need to surrender the fight and hand over the care to his or her own appropriate Anonymous Fellowship. In due course, in recovery, the primary sufferer and the friend or family member can be reunited in a happier and more fulfilling relationship than ever before.

Childhood Influences

1.	At birth we have little intellectual capacity but enormous emotional capacity. Gradually, as we develop through childhood and adolescence, we increase our intellectual capacity. Hopefully, we retain much of our emotional capacity but much of our "education" is directed towards suppressing it. When traumatic events occur, they create tape-recordings in the brain in the ratio of intellectual to emotional capacity at the age

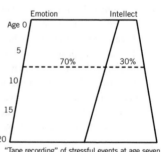

"Tape recording" of stressful events at age seven

one is at the time of that event. When these tape-recordings replay at a later age, in response to a similar stimulus, they do so in that same ratio. Thus, the earlier in life the initial trauma, the more dramatic is the emotional effect and the less available is our intellect to modify it. In adult life we cannot modify our childhood tape-recordings but we can come to recognise them (e.g. "abuse", "abandonment" etc.) so that we can influence our reaction to them even though they replay with all the emotional intensity of the time of their creation.

2. Much misguided psychotherapy is directed at understanding early childhood experiences, as if mere intellectual understanding could resolve emotional imprints. The more intellectual (or less emotionally free) the psychotherapist, the greater the danger of this misconception. We cannot think ourselves out of pain or depression. "Cognitive-behavioural" approaches sound attractive to clever doctors and psychotherapists but they don't work for emotionally damaged patients. They are particularly pointless when used in combination with mood-altering medications such as tranquillisers, sleeping tablets or anti-depressants that further suppress the capacity of the brain to feel for itself.

3. A particularly dangerous falsehood is the concept of "multi-generational shame" being the underlying cause of addictive behaviour. In this, each generation shames the next through abuse and abandonment, and makes the recipients "co-dependent" (whatever that may mean). This leads to a tendency towards use of mood-altering substances, behaviours and relationships. Thus, we are encouraged to understand that our parents caused our addiction but were not at fault in doing so. Further, all we have to do to avoid handing on addictive tendencies to our children is to ensure that we do not abuse or abandon them. This is all absolute poppycock - and nasty with it.

4. Early childhood trauma should be examined in early recovery only in so far as it helps to unblock us in our emotional redevelopment. To look at it in greater depth at this time simply re-traumatises us. One of the functions of treatment centres is to help us to deal with various blocks (grief, guilt, shame, anger, despair etc.) appropriately so that we can move on rather than remain forever stuck, paralysed by the all-pervading influence of these blocks. The appropriate time to look back in depth at early childhood experiences is when we are about six years clean from use of any mood-altering substance, behaviour or relationship and fully involved in working the Twelve Steps on a day-to-day basis. At that time we can recognise that our parents, or other people who did damaging things to us, may have been addicts just like us and we can view them with understanding and genuine compassion.

5. When we think back to childhood experiences, and replay our tapes, we re-implant them in our long-term memory. Through frequency of use, they grow in influence. The Twelve Step programme helps us to take responsibility for ourselves in the adult world. No longer do we clutter up our heads with childhood events and resentments. We free our minds and hearts for use in the present.

Environmental Influences

1. Everyone on earth is under considerable influence from various environments. Some people, particularly using addicts, try to blame environmental factors for all our own woes, rather than take responsibility for ourselves. Everything was wrong: our upbringing, culture, society, religious and political and educational influences, family, home, work - all of these damaged us. Well, maybe some of them (mother, perhaps, or a place we once lived in) were perfect - but nowadays it has all changed for the worse and we believe that nothing is really right.

2. Yet when we look at other people, even our own brothers and sisters living under similar environmental influences, we find that they do not necessarily share the same problems. Many of our difficulties go with us rather than with our various environments. Naturally, as our addictive disease tightens its grip, our environmental problems increase. As we drop through various social and cultural dividing lines, we do indeed have progressively more problems with our various environments and it is indeed true that progressively more of the people around us are just like us. "Everyone drinks (or uses drugs or whatever) as much as I do" is our favourite justification. Our environments change as we change and we modify our attitudes to fit our new behaviour.

3. Sometimes we get trapped by particular environmental influences and we cling to them as causes or potential cures of our problems:

    i.   Our parents, or other childhood carers, often come in for special criticism. Addicts, and often their counsellors or "therapists" frequently give parents a very bad press, instead of recognising that they often did the best they could with difficult charges and that we ourselves will find parenting, and other areas of responsibility for children, to be no easier than they did;
    ii. Cultural and social influences may be interpreted as all good or all bad. We may try to change ourselves by running from one environment to another - but at all times we take ourselves with us;
    iii. We may seek political, religious, occupational or educational (and especially crackpot therapy) changes to help us with the various difficulties that we believe determine the way we feel. We get better only when we take full responsibility for our own thoughts, feelings, actions and reactions.

4. The one genuine significant environmental influence for addicts is that a particular environment may determine which particular addictive outlets we discover.

    i.   In early childhood, if something leads to the need for mood-alteration, sugar and white flour may be the only mood-altering substances available to us;
    ii. If our background is one in which alcohol, drugs or nicotine are commonplace, then we may believe that their use is normal for us;
    iii. If we are encouraged towards particular behaviours in the belief that they are healthy, we may be convinced of their virtue and unaware of the harm they can cause;

iv. If our social circumstances are particularly stressful, we may be prescribed mood-altering medication by a "sympathetic" doctor;

v. If we discover the mood-altering effect of particular relationships, then we may seek to find other relationships that have similar power to help us to feel better, even if the beneficial effects are transient and ultimately illusory.

5. Distorted or damaging environmental influences can be helped with appropriate counselling, enabling us to put down our misconceptions and resentments and move on into the adult world, whereas genetic influences require continuing treatment with the Twelve Step programme.

6. In recovery we come to accept that there may be any number of things that are "wrong" with our various environments but it is up to us either to come to terms with them or change them. Blaming other people or various environmental influences gets us nowhere.

The Addictive Family

1. The archetypal addictive family tends to be seen as having an alcoholic father, a compulsive overeating mother making everyone happy with her compulsive helping, and four children: the hero, the scapegoat, the lost child and the mascot or clown. These stereotypes describe various personality types and are therefore interesting but it cannot be argued that they are particular to addictive families. Nor can it be argued that each of these childhood personality types has a particular risk of developing addictive behaviour in later life. Addictive disease is probably genetically inherited and can affect any personality type and appear in any environment.

2. There are probably three stages in the development of addiction:

i. Genetic inheritance. If you haven't got it you can nonetheless still damage yourself and other people through stupid use of addictive substances or processes, but you will never become an addict other than merely physiologically. You may go through transient withdrawal symptoms, after a period of sustained use, but you will not have the craving to return to use. It is this craving to return to using the substances and processes of addiction that is typical of addicts. The madness of addictive disease is that, for comfort, we go back to the source of many of our problems.

ii. Traumatic events that stimulate and sensitise the underlying addictive potential. It is important to recognise that these traumatic events do not "cause" the subsequent addictive behaviour. Their importance is in their timing: the particular addictive outlets that are turned to will depend upon what is available at the time of the trauma. For example, early childhood trauma often leads to the development of eating disorders in those who have the genetically inherited addictive potential, because the mood-altering properties of sugar and refined carbohydrates are readily available to children.

iii. Exposure to mood-altering substances, behaviour or relationships that "work" for that individual. Most addicts find three or four, or even more, addictive outlets at the same time. Environmental influences play a great part in determining which addictive outlets a particular addict will discover. In due course, as the addiction takes hold, the addict may fall through the floor of his or her social group and come to live in progressively more degrading environments as one loss piles upon another. However, it is important to emphasise that the environment is a consequence of the addiction, not the cause.

Naturally, in an addictive family all three components are usually present in the development of any addiction. It would therefore be surprising if a child who inherited the genetic potential did not subsequently develop addictive behaviour of his or her own. Long-term Scandinavian adoption studies show that children taken at birth from addictive families and brought up by non-addictive families still have a much higher incidence of addiction than in the general population, thus demonstrating that nature is a more reliable predictor of addiction than nurture.

3. Nevertheless, if we are members of an addictive family, there is a great deal that we can do to protect our children. Providing a loving and enthusiastic environment may not prevent them from becoming addicts but they will always know that there is a better life to be had than the life of a using addict. Ultimately that contrast will draw them to want to change their behaviour.

4. Perhaps the most difficult thing for addictive families to accept is that sometimes an addict doesn't change his or her behaviour and doesn't get into recovery. (Using prescription medicines is not recovery; it is simply an alternative addiction.) When the founders of Alcoholics Anonymous described addictive behaviour as "cunning, baffling and powerful", they were right. Despite all that we have learned and continue to learn about addictive disease, it always will be cunning, baffling and powerful. We simply do the best we can and leave the rest to God.

The Family Programme

1. Most family members initially want to find out:

    i.   how to prove that their family member or friend isn't really an addict;
    ii. what caused the "behavioural problems";
    iii. what they could have done to prevent them or could do now to cure them.

Often family members are upset or even offended at the diagnosis of addiction. They may be even more concerned by the suggestion that they themselves might benefit from some supportive understanding. Yet that alone is precisely what needs to be provided because that is what is positively helpful to both the addicts and their families.

2. Acceptance that a loved one does indeed suffer from addictive disease and that there is nothing whatever one could have done to prevent it in the past, or even do in the present and future, is exceedingly painful. The feeling of impotence compounds any feelings of anger, sadness, disappointment and shame. These feelings, while understandable, are mostly inappropriate.

3. The aims of the twin therapeutic programmes (for the addicts themselves and for their families, loved ones, friends or other concerned persons) are to give each a sense of understanding of, and responsibility for, their own thoughts, feelings, actions and reactions. Understanding of each other comes later. Furthermore, the concept of being responsible for someone else is gradually displaced through the treatment programme by the understanding of what it means to be responsible to that person.

4. Some family members may themselves be compulsive helpers or even have primary addictions of their own. They may require treatment in their own right, quite distinct from the family programme.

5. The purpose of the family programme is to clarify an understanding of addictive disease in all its forms, both from the perspective of the addict and of the family member. Each needs first an understanding of self and later an understanding of the other.

6. Recovery rates for addicted patients are improved significantly when their family members commit themselves thoroughly to the family programme.

7. Addicts are not the only ones to feel pain or to have problems and they are not the only ones to benefit from supportive help, understanding and challenge.

Prevention

1. It would be nice to believe that love, education and punishment would work in the prevention of addictive behaviour. They don't. They should, but they don't. We should, of course, provide an example of love and an environment of love and we should, of course, educate all children on the nature of addictive substances and their dangers. But that won't prevent addiction: those who need to learn won't listen and those who do listen don't have the same level of need to do so. We should, of course, give appropriate punishment for aberrant behaviour but ultimately, if that is all we do in confronting addictive disease, we may simply be punishing people for being ill and that is inappropriate.

2. Addictive disease needs to be diagnosed for what it is, rather than hidden in a welter of spurious diagnoses such as hyperactivity, attention deficit disorder or depression.

3.   Potential addicts can be diagnosed in childhood on the following characteristics:

    i.   Coming from an addictive family.
    ii.   Highly manipulative, more so than normal children.
    iii.   Extreme mood swings for no truly justifiable reason.
    iv.   A sense of personal isolation even when surrounded by friends.
    v.   Easily hurt and emotionally fragile.
    vi.   Easily frustrated and dissatisfied.

4.   It is commonplace in medical practice for children (and adults) to be targeted when we know that they have specific risks. This same principle should apply in addictive families. Not all children in addictive families will necessarily be at risk of developing overt addictions in later life (they may not inherit the particular genes) but they have a higher chance of doing so. This is where resources should be focused.

5.   When the human genome is fully worked out by the year 2010 there will be clamours that potential addicts should be identified and aborted before birth. This would remove many highly creative individuals upon whom society depends. It is also unnecessary because the Twelve Step programme treats additive disease in a wholly satisfactory manner on a continuing basis, just as many other chronic illnesses are treated satisfactorily on a continuing basis. For what other conditions would there be similar clamours to abort? Where would we draw the line?

6.   Those children most at risk of becoming addicts need to be specifically educated in the nature of addictive disease (in all its outlets) and in the processes of recovery. Ideally they should become familiar with working a Twelve Step programme before they have any need for it in the specific treatment of addictive behaviour.

7.   The widespread belief that drugs are "pushed", or that addictive behaviour comes from disturbed family or social backgrounds, is incorrect. Those of us who are addicts by nature have often been exceedingly well nurtured and much loved. Our sense of inner emptiness (for no justifiable social reason) leads us to draw addictive substances, processes and relationships towards ourselves. Addictive disease is rooted in us and in all our society, just as in any other. We should identify and help those who have it.

Policy for Schools

1.   School policy on addiction is generally an absolute disaster:

    i.   It tends to focus only upon illegal drugs and, in girls' schools, anorexia;
    ii.   As a means of prevention, it relies upon education on dangers and upon the futile exhortation to "just say no";
    iii.   It fails to concentrate on those who have the greatest risk;
    iv.   It is generally too late.

2. An appropriate policy must first and foremost be to educate the school staff:

   i.   The concept of "pushers hanging around the school gates" is fatuous. Children generally obtain addictive substances through their own family and friends. The major suppliers to schools are its own pupils;

   ii.   The staff themselves are just as likely as the pupils to be addicts of one kind or another;

   iii. The school medical staff may not have had any education at all on addictive disease as such and may still see the excessive use of mood-altering substances, behaviours or relationships as bad behaviour rather than illness;

   iv. Expulsion of pupils caught using illegal drugs merely chips off the tip of the iceberg. While it is perfectly appropriate to give consequences to addictive behaviour, this particular policy in isolation does nothing for the welfare of the afflicted children. That sets a poor social example.

3. School policy should be formulated on the following lines:

   i.   It should examine all addictive or compulsive behaviour, irrespective of whether the substances, processes and relationships are legal or illegal, recreational or medicinal, normally classified simply as foods or even generally seen as healthy pursuits;

   ii.   Education should focus upon the nature and identification of addictive disease and recovery. Simply telling secondary school children about the dangers of drugs is pointless, however much their parents may wish this to be part of the school curriculum. Children mostly already know from each other not only the dangers but also the pleasures. They also know many of their own number who have taken illegal substances without ill effect;

   iii. Schools may sometimes feel that family background is none of their business. They may express concern for children who come from disturbed backgrounds and they may believe that environmental factors at home have a considerable influence at school. However, schools tend to fight shy of considering, let alone enquiring about, possible genetic influence. The noting of parental and grandparental addictive or compulsive behaviour in any form should be a basic part of any school medical assessment. Children who have addicts of any kind in their families are those who are most likely to be addicts themselves. These children need special care and attention in order to intervene as early as possible in the development of addictive disease. This is healthy for the school as well as for the children themselves. For the rest of the pupils there is certainly no harm in telling them about the dangers of mood-altering substances, behaviours and relationships (idiosyncratic responses can occur at any time such as after one inhalation of solvents or one tablet of Ecstacy or, for that matter, one aspirin or one tablet of penicillin). However, this education needs to be on the risks of any addictive substance, including nicotine, sugar and alcohol, the three most damaging substances of all, and also on the dangers of addictive processes and relationships;

   iv. Education on addictive disease and recovery should begin in primary schools.

Why ever not? That is when we have the best chance of identifying addictive disease before children have discovered the use of mood-altering substances, behaviours and relationships and done damage to themselves and other people. That is a good policy.

Policy for Employers

1. Whatever policy is adopted for the workplace, it has to be applied universally from boardroom to shopfloor. Otherwise it will always be seen solely as a disciplinary process rather than also as a health issue. Discipline will naturally tend to be resisted by staff whereas a health measure has at least a chance of universal support.

2. Every employee has the right to safety in the workplace and to the knowledge that everything possible has been done to achieve it. Mood-altering substances and processes cloud judgement. Addicts can jeopardise the lives of other people as well as their own. Companies can be destroyed more commonly by poor management than by strikes or by other problems with the workforce. Addictive behaviour, such as compulsive gambling on the markets or on risky ventures, or addictive relationships (e.g. seeking power for its own sake) can wipe out companies altogether. The Exxon Valdez was driven on to the rocks by a drunken sea captain. The secrets of the Polaris submarine programme were betrayed by the Walker family in exchange for money for drugs, risking the security of the entire Western world. Old established banks have been sold off as the result of the activities of rogue traders and the carelessness or complicity of their supervisors. Dynasties that have been built up over generations have collapsed in a few years in the hands of an addict of one kind or another.

3. Companies have greater risk of being put out of business by their own addictive staff than by any competitor.

    i.   The Confederation of British Industry emphasises that staff with established drug problems cause damage through loss of time, loss of efficiency, mistakes and accidents;
    ii. As long ago as 1987, Professor Alan Maynard of the Department of Health Economics, York University, estimated the annual cost of alcohol misuse alone at £1.6 billion, including £641 million cost of sickness absence;
    iii. The Trades Union Congress in its guidelines for a workplace policy for problem drinking, pointed out that "the majority of problem drinkers are not down and outs but are to be found in employment, often tolerated by colleagues and management until their condition worsens to a point of chronic incompetence whereupon they either leave due to deteriorating health or are simply dismissed. The costs to the individual, to the employer and to society are considerable and there are no benefits".

4. Dismissed addictive employees are likely to be replaced by new recruits who also have risks of addictive disease. Pre-employment urinary drug screens at Owens Corning Fibreglass have never produced a positive figure of less than ten per cent even when prospective employees have been warned in advance that their urine would be tested for illegal substances. The drug problem is universal in our society and no company or institution can afford to close its eyes to it and believe itself to be immune. Indeed, the medical advisers to schools, companies and other institutions have just the same risks as anyone else of being addicted.

5. Random urinary drug screens appear superficially to be sensible but they focus on only one addictive behaviour and may therefore give a false sense of security. They are an expensive method of obtaining inadequate information.

   A better method of observing more significant data that is already available is to look at personnel records for the following:

   i. absenteeism and poor time-keeping;
   ii. accidents at work;
   iii. accidents elsewhere (if known);
   iv. road accidents;
   v. disputes and disturbed relationships with colleagues;
   vi. divorce and marital disturbances (if known);
   vii. drunk-driving offences;
   viii. other legal problems;
   ix. previous employment records of various problems;
   x. failure to maintain professional standards, being at the same time perfectionist in some things and amazingly casual in others;
   xi. disturbed relationships with suppliers, clients and other outside agencies;
   xii. any concern expressed by colleagues, clients or other people on the individual's drinking habits or general behaviour;
   xiii. episodes of recurrent minor illnesses and mood disorders with recurrent recourse to medication;
   xiv. poor general health or fitness;
   xv. financial problems;
   xvi. erratic performance at work or failure to achieve the level of performance that could reasonably be expected from qualifications and previous experience;
   xvii. the tendency to become more involved in drink-related activities and less in other social activities;
   xviii. difficulties in concentration and in accuracy of memory.

6. Staff whose performance is impaired should be given the straight choice between disciplinary and clinical approaches. (This would generally have the support of Trades Unions and other staff representatives.) The details of the clinical approach should be determined by the company, rather than by the individual who will more than likely slip through the net by obtaining a medical certificate labelled "depression" or "work stress" and a prescription for Prozac from his or her own doctor or psychiatrist.

7. The prime purpose of companies is to produce profits for their shareholders. The prime purpose of other institutions is to deliver whatever service it is that they have to offer. In each case the costs of appropriate intervention and clinical treatment have been shown by long-term studies to be significantly less than the costs of ignoring the problem or simply waiting until major damage has been done before taking action. Chief Executive Officers, Finance Directors, Personnel Directors and the heads of other institutions would be well advised to become familiar with the processes involved in addictive disease and recovery, rather than simply trying to keep illegal substances out of their environment - which is nowadays probably impossible.

8. The problem of addictive disease is absolutely vast and it is not going to go away. Under the right guidance, recovery is possible.

Global Policy on Addiction

1. Addictive Disease

1. The tendency towards addictive behaviour is probably genetically inherited, affecting some people but not others. It is probably caused by defects in the neurotransmission systems of the mood centres of the brain.

2. Affected people are born with a tendency to be depressed for no valid reason. They discover for themselves, through environmental influences, the mood-altering properties of some substances and processes. These make life seem worth living but the effects wear off and therefore their use has to be repeated.

3. In time tolerance develops so that the unit dose has to be increased in order to obtain the same mood-altering effect.

4. When the damaging consequences of use mount up, the addict gets to the stage where he or she cannot live with the addictive substance or process but cannot live without it.

5. Some addicts change to another addiction: most addicts have three or four addictive outlets of various kinds (alcohol, drugs, nicotine, prescription drugs, gambling etc.) at the same time.

6. Personal values are adjusted to match the behaviour that is uncontrollable.

7. In ultimate despair, suicide or death through accidents or violence are common.

2. Inappropriate Treatment

1. Methadone is simply an alternative addiction. It does nothing to heal the underlying mood disorder. It is not safe: in the UK more people now die of the effects of Methadone than die from use of heroin. Some children are now introduced to opiates through blackmarket Methadone obtained through sale of legal prescriptions. Addicts rarely restrict their drug use to Methadone alone: they commonly augment their supply. Crime is not reduced: Methadone is now simply another drug alongside heroin, cocaine, Ecstasy and the rest.

2. There is no distinction between hard and soft drugs, nor in the use of recreational or prescribed drugs, such as anti-depressants, tranquillisers, painkillers or sleeping tablets. Addicts will use whatever they find has a mood-altering effect, irrespective of textbook definitions of addiction.

3. Addicts are commonly misdiagnosed as suffering from depression and then prescribed anti-depressants and other drugs. This compounds rather than relieves the addiction. The dose of these prescribed drugs is commonly progressively increased.

4. Needle exchange and other techniques in pursuit of "harm minimisation" achieve no such end result. Addicts on maintenance programmes may not have the same risk of AIDS and hepatitis (unless they augment their drug supply and use contaminated equipment opportunistically) but they have the same risk of damage or death from other complications of addiction as before.

5. It is unethical to write off one group of patients (by prescribing Methadone for addicts) in order to protect another group (those members of the heterosexual population who use prostitutes). AIDS would not spread into the heterosexual population if people did not sleep around. Addicts deserve to be treated with the same concern and respect as other people and they should be given the opportunity to become totally drug-free.

3. The Addict's Perspective.

1. In pursuit of mood-alteration (in order to feel normal, not just "high" on occasions), addicts will draw mood-altering substances to them: these do not have to be "pushed".

2. Addicts exist in all societies and in all walks of life. Major addictive and immensely damaging substances such as alcohol, sugar and nicotine are commonly legal and socially acceptable.

3. Even supposing the policies of crop substitution, increasing the efforts of police and customs officers and instilling zero tolerance were to be totally successful, addicts will still find ways of obtaining mood-altering drugs of one kind or another.

4. The basic psychopathology of addictive disease is denial. The alcoholic on the park bench believes that he or she has a social and financial problem rather than one with alcohol - which is seen as a comfort and benefit. The drug addict believes that he or she is not addicted because it is still possible to give up. There is no insight into the fact that the true nature of addiction is the return to use of drugs despite previous damage.

5. Helping people to come off drugs is relatively easy. Addicts will con people otherwise because they want sympathy for their problem, they enjoy the drama, and often they simply want to prolong their supply. The exception is withdrawal from prescription drugs which is difficult, both physically and psychologically. Helping addicts to learn how to stay off drugs is very difficult and is the major challenge of the Minnesota (Twelve Step) Method of treatment.

6. The only successful motive for the addict to change addictive behaviour is when the pain of continuing to use is greater than the perceived pain of cessation.

4. The Recovery Perspective.

1. Addicts know about addiction: doctors and sociologists often merely observe its characteristics and consequences.

2. All addictive use and behaviour has to be confronted at the same time. There is little point in treating one addiction while leaving others rampant. Some immediate damage may be avoided by half measures but nothing is gained in the long term: relapse is almost inevitable if any addictive tendency is left untreated.

3. Love, education and punishment neither prevent nor treat addiction. Love is a fine example, education is sensible, and punishment for aberrant behaviour is appropriate - but none has any affect on addiction, any more than they would on appendicitis or schizophrenia.

4. Addicts get better when they believe they can. They can be given this insight only by other (former) addicts. No one else will be trusted or followed.

5. There is a fundamental difference between abstinence (merely stopping using particular addictive substances for a time) and recovery (working the Twelve Step programme of an Anonymous Fellowship such as Narcotics Anonymous on a continuing basis).

6. The appropriate long-term alternative to mood-altering drugs or processes is when one addict reaches out to help another anonymously. The donor stays clean; the recipient may or may not.

7. Commonly behind each addict is a compulsive helper, matching the addict's need to be "fixed" with the helper's need to be needed.

8. Large numbers of people use addictive substances without being addicted to them. Alcohol provides an obvious example but the same principle can apply to any drug. Identifying specific addictive use is therefore vital. This is done, for example, on the PROMIS Questionnaires which cover all forms of addictive behaviour. The crucial issue is not which, or how much, addictive substance or process is used but why.

5. Policy Suggestions.

1. Continue crop substitution policies as at present.

2. Continue to increase the efforts of police and customs officers.

3. Introduce, or continue, policies of zero tolerance for addictive behaviour.

4. Encourage in medical schools, as well as in general schools, an educational programme not so much on drugs as specifically on addictive disease and recovery.

5. Encourage in general education an awareness that the most dangerous drugs in modern society are alcohol, sugar (the addictive substance produced by removal of healthy fibre) and nicotine, killing twenty, forty and sixty times as many people as all the illegal drugs put together.

6. Target, for particular education and help, those families in whom there is an established history of addictive or compulsive behaviour (alcoholism, drug addiction, eating disorders etc.) Not all children in an addictive family will be equally at risk. Addictive potential can be seen in children as young as four years old who have particular behavioural characteristics (highly manipulative, mood swings for no reason, a sense of isolation even among friends, easily hurt and emotionally fragile, easily frustrated and disappointed).

7. Abandon policies of Methadone maintenance and needle substitution and get rid of the concept of "harm minimisation". The only effective harm minimisation is total abstinence.

8. Drop financial and social services support for addicts.
   Question: What's green and gets you high?
   Answer : A Social Security cheque.

9. Help should be given in the form of compulsory residential treatment in a Minnesota Method (Twelve Step) treatment centre. The costs are less than the costs of prison or hospital. Treatment programmes are vital in prisons but should preferably be used long before prison is ever considered necessary.

10. Adopt a uniform policy on the use of mood-altering substances.
    e.g. All use of any mood-altering substance (nicotine, alcohol, heroin, cocaine, cannabis, Ecstasy, amphetamines etc.) should be legal, provided that its use involves

no risk to other people. This is often the existing policy for alcohol.

11. Adopt a uniform policy on the management of disorders of perception, e.g. the Mental Health Act in the UK is already used to protect patients with acute psychoses from damaging themselves or other people. The same Mental Health Act should be extended to cover addictive disease.

12. The elucidation of the human genome in the next decade will probably result in the possibility of pre-natal determination of the potential for addictive disease. The call for eugenics should be resisted: addicts are some of society's most creative individuals. Their children should not be aborted but should be targeted for educational special need.

13. The Anonymous Fellowships are free to members and they decline outside contributions from state or private resources. They constitute an enormous free resource for prevention of relapse. Widespread public awareness of their existence and of their principles is vital.

14. Most difficult of all, compulsive helpers (be they family members, doctors and nurses, social workers, probation officers, politicians or whatever) who bail out the addicts from the consequences of their behaviour need to be shown that they damage the chance of the addicts getting into lasting recovery. The risk of taking a difficult decision today has to be shown to be less than the much larger risks involved in delaying that decision.

15. Influence the press (!) and the medical profession (!!) to drop all ideas that addiction comes from stressful social circumstances. There are millions of people who have endured similar social deprivation or trauma yet have not become addicts.

16. Focus attention on those most at risk (those with a family history of addictive or compulsive behaviour) rather than on giving exhaustive information to all and sundry in a misguided attempt to educate through fear. Addicts surmount fear, whereas the normal population can be damaged by it. Idiosyncratic reactions to drugs (dying after one Ecstasy tablet or, for that matter, one aspirin) will always occur and should not be used for general education on the risks of drugs. Children are already aware of many contemporaries who use drugs regularly yet so far have suffered no damaging consequences. Emphasising idiosyncratic responses is therefore counterproductive. Children can sensibly be taught the dangers of alcohol, sugar, nicotine and drugs alongside the dangers of road accidents or drowning. This is a different subject from teaching them about addictive disease and recovery, which may be of minimal interest to most families but, as with many clinical conditions, is of vital interest to those most likely to be affected.

Health

1. Stop smoking.

2. Stop smoking. That's the only thing that really matters: all other improvements in health pale into insignificance by comparison. The heart transplant programme, the medical and surgical treatments for chronic bronchitis and cancer of the lung, the amputations for arterial disease, the whole caboosh, are not the proper way to run a Health Service; a disease service maybe but certainly not a health service. Concerns over cigarette advertising are misplaced: cannabis, amphetamines, Ecstasy and cocaine are almost as widely used, particularly among the young, yet have no advertising whatever. The training of doctors and other health workers should focus to a much greater extent on understanding and treating addictive behaviour (learning in particular about treating nicotine addiction, the biggest killer of all) because behind every major killing disease is the significant influence of one addictive behaviour or another. Telling people to stop smoking and stop doing other damaging things to themselves is all very well - but they need to know how to do that and it is not much help if the helping professions don't know either.

3. Beware of accidents. Wear seat belts even in the back: why take an avoidable risk of the most likely cause of death in young people? Learn to swim and always wear life belts when appropriate. Be aware of dangerous sports, not just boxing, a relatively minor if deliberate risk, but the much greater risks of rugby football, rock climbing and horse-riding, a particularly dangerous sport with young girls going down like ninepins every weekend in the cause of "healthy pursuits". Protect your eyes and ears in sports and other activities where they are likely to be damaged. Fix the carpets, particularly on the stairs and check all the electrical appliances regularly. Unplug the TV when not in use. Accidents of one kind or another in the home exact a terrible toll. Accidents at work may be someone else's responsibility - but it is better not to have to go to the hospital or the courts, or even the grave, in the first place. Watch out!

4. Cut down on alcohol consumption. If you can't control it (try drinking two glasses of wine at lunch time every day for a week and nothing more in the rest of the day), then go to Alcoholics Anonymous. There are plenty of other pleasures in life for those who are sufficiently sober to enjoy them.

5. Have a healthy mixed diet with plenty of fish and cereals, fresh fruit and vegetables. Cut out sugar and white flour. A low-fibre diet is the principal cause of many intestinal conditions and second only to cigarette smoking in cardiovascular disease. A high-fat diet is not as significant as it is made out to be: as a nation we eat the same amount of animal fat now as we did at the turn of the last century, whereas we eat one hundred times the amount of sugar.

6. Respect the delicacy and intricacy of body tissues, particularly those of the brain. If we don't respect ourselves, and particularly the clarity of our thought, and the range

of our feelings, then what do we respect? Avoiding things that we know perfectly well to be damaging to ourselves comes a long way ahead of trying to do things that are "healthy". After all, by and large, the human body looks after itself perfectly well without cranky diets full of totally unnecessary "health foods", vitamins, trace elements and heaven knows what else that serve only to provide profits to the manufacturers, fees to avaricious private doctors, and fuel for an obsessive nature that would rather not look at emotional problems and at inadequate relationships.

7. Keep body weight within a lifetime range of eight pounds and keep fit with regular daily exercise of no more than twenty minutes and with one day off each week. Avoid dieting regimes; if they worked at all, the dieting industry wouldn't be as massive as it is.

8. Take Government Health warnings (other than on cigarette smoking - although even there the policy seems muddled) with a pinch of salt - if salt is still permissible in the Nanny State. They made a complete mess of AIDS and still try to frighten everybody over something that in the UK is primarily a problem for gays and needle-using drugs addicts. If they want to keep AIDS out of the heterosexual population, then telling people not to screw hookers would be a good start - or would government law officers find that a bit difficult to say as they cruise around Kings Cross? They made an absolute dog's breakfast of BSE, destroying the beef industry for fear that someone might be blamed for not warning the public about an insignificant risk (while nobody in government or the civil service has yet been blamed for suggesting that cows, instead of eating grass, should be fed the ground-up remains of diseased sheep). They kill more people with Methadone than ever died from using heroin. They had hysteria over listeria in soft cheeses that may damage pregnant women but which are an acceptable and delicious risk for the rest of us - as are so many things that they try to warn us against. Anyway, what is the current advice on cholesterol, now that it has been found that a low-fat diet may decrease heart disease but increase the risk of strokes and suicide? Does it depend on the day of the week? It certainly seems so.

9. Beware of doctors. We do too much and prescribe too frequently, particularly broad-spectrum antibiotics and mood-altering drugs such as tranquillisers, sleeping tablets and anti-depressants. Whatever happened to the concept of self-reliance? Have we so little respect for patients' powers of resistance against illness and infection that we throw drugs at them without even being asked? Have we so little time for or interest in people that we are no longer prepared to listen to them and provide simple human comfort and reassurance? But do, however, use doctors for regular inoculations and simple regular check-ups for asymptomatic conditions such as raised blood pressure, anaemia, early diabetes or thyroid deficiency, glaucoma, skin or colon cancer, kidney problems and disorders of the reproductive organs, such as cancer of the prostate, ovary or cervix. Know your family medical history so that you are aware of your most probable risks.

10. Forget about "alternative" therapies. They are no more appropriate than traditional pharmacological remedies. Hocus pocus is no substitute for poison. Both approaches are often unnecessary: the body largely heals itself.

11. For emotional problems avoid all "passive" therapies, where something is done to you or for you. Personal issues can only be resolved, sometimes with some careful experienced guidance, by personal commitment to necessary change.

12. Health is, above all, an attitude of mind. It has nothing to do with treating largely fictitious conditions such as ME, food allergies, vitamin and trace-element deficiencies, intestinal candidiasis, repetitive strain injury and the like. It has a great deal to do with being honest, open-minded, willing, considerate and kind and also accepting full responsibility for our own thoughts, feelings, actions and reactions. Nobody "makes" us feel or do anything. Life is a system of choices. It is up to each one of us to ensure that the choices we make are in the best interests of our bodies, minds and spirits.

> "Happy the man and happy he alone,
> He who can call today his own.
> He who, secure within, can say
> 'Tomorrow do thy worst - for I have lived today'."
> - Sir Thomas More

And healthy too.

Isolation

1. Addictive disease wants each one of us to be isolated, wants us to itself and ultimately wants us dead. It may seem strange to anthropomorphise addictive disease in this way but it certainly feels as if it is alive in its power to control, drive and manipulate us towards our own destruction.

2. As addicts, we seek the perfect friend who will totally understand us, realising that our motives are good even if our behaviour slips at times, accept that we have special circumstances that need to be taken into consideration, and stand by us - right or wrong. No one comes up to this demanding specification except ourselves.

3. In isolation we rule our own kingdom, spiritually bankrupt. Nobody can criticise us or control us because nobody is there. The determination to prove ourselves correct on all issues eventually results in people giving up on us.

4. In the Anonymous Fellowships and in Minnesota Method treatment centres we discover the remarkable fact that there are other people just like us. They may not necessarily have come from the same background, nor done the same things we have done, but their description of their feelings - and their attempts to control them - matches ours. This bond gives us hope.

5. In time we meet progressively more people in the Anonymous Fellowships who are also just like us in special ways. It feels as if we are all members of one tribe - and indeed we are: we have a common natural feature, a common practical philosophy, and a common goal.

6. If we look for similarities we can see them and this keeps us true to the common purpose of helping us all to get better from our addictive disease. If we look for differences we can certainly find them: one would hope so - we are individuals. However, our addictive disease can seize on this and drive us back into isolation.

7. Ultimately we need to develop an awareness that our similarities with other people extend well beyond the Anonymous Fellowships. The Fellowships are a bridge to normal living, not an end in themselves. In fact, normal living involves accepting other people's differences as well as their similarities.

8. When, finally, we come to accept other people as they are, and become less critical of them, we come closer to accepting ourselves and we have no need to isolate ourselves.

Brain-Washing

1. By the time we have got to the stage of needing treatment for our addictive disease, our brains need a good wash. They are super-saturated with self-pity, blame, resentment, self-justification, rationalisation, intellectualisation and all kinds of mental and emotional garbage. On top of all that we may be drugged with alcohol, sugar, recreational drugs, nicotine, caffeine and a pot-pourri of prescription medications. In short, our brains are a mess.

2. It is ironic that at this stage we look at the words of the Twelve Steps and actually complain that they are an attempt at brainwashing. So they should be!

3. Looking more closely in the Big Book of Alcoholics Anonymous we note in the preamble that the Twelve Steps are "merely suggested" and in the postscript it says that "no one among us is capable of perfect adherence to these Steps". In particular, we note that the word "God" is followed by the italicised phrase "as you understand Him". Furthermore, financial donations are voluntary and there are vital traditions that Anonymous Fellowships reject outside contributions and that there are no leaders. Yet we accuse the Anonymous Fellowships of being a cult that wants to control us and preach to us.

4. It takes time to see that it was addictive disease that controlled us and filled our heads with its own propaganda, saying that this or that was "not addictive" or "normal behaviour" or even "our right as individuals". In fact the last thing that addictive disease enables us to be is individual: we become as boringly predictable as any other addict.

5. For years our heads have repeated the mantra of addictive disease: "I am special and different", "Poor me", "I deserve it (whatever I want)", so that we have become programmed like robots.

6. The Anonymous Fellowships are voluntary. As the name implies, there is no register of membership, no knowledge of people's surnames, addresses or occupations. There are no attempts whatever to have influence upon anything other than addictive behaviour. Solely in that aspect of life is there a focus on group adherence to simple principles of thought, feeling and behaviour - because it was found that they work in putting our addictive disease into remission when nothing else had worked.

7. As our minds gradually clear, when we stop poisoning our capacity to be ourselves, when our brains are washed appropriately, we are freed from the captivity of addictive disease and given freedom of choice of thoughts, feelings, actions and reactions in continuing recovery.

God

1. Through the telescope we see the wonders of the structure of the universe. Though the microscope we see the wonders of the structure of animate and inanimate objects. As science progresses, superstition diminishes - or so it should.

2. Man creates God in order to explain the inexplicable. We have a fear of the unknown and of our irrelevance. We seek ultimate answers because we find it difficult to live with open-ended questions. But surely that is the beautiful miracle of existence: we don't know the answers to even the basic questions of where we come from, what we are doing and where we are going. It is only when Man puts his own intellect at the centre of the universe that we diminish our world and the lives we live. Then, in the names of various One True Gods, we set about killing each other.

3. Yet the concept of a Higher Power than self is central to the Twelve Step programme. Take away the spiritual component of the Twelve Steps and there is nothing left. We have to find a Higher Power because otherwise we are our own Higher Power and we know from dreadful experience that that doesn't work. Following our own perceptions and our own way of doing things is precisely what got us into the mess we are in. We have discovered that we are powerless to change our compulsive behaviour: it wouldn't be compulsive if we could. We desperately need a Higher Power than self because we shall die if we don't find one - and that is exactly what our addictive disease wants: it wants us isolated, lord of our own exclusive kingdom and, best of all, dead.

4. We come alive when we interrelate with others. Spiritual mathematics has its own rules: $1+0 = 0$; $1+1 = 3$. By ourselves we are nothing (just try it to verify it: we go mad if we are desensitised in a blank room). Alongside other people we develop the capacity to create more than we could ever achieve individually. In this way other

people are indeed a Higher Power than self. Making any individual person into a God would be foolish, yet political, social, economic, therapeutic and religious gurus abound, leaving carnage in their wake. But a Group Of Drunks (who have discovered how to stay sober when we can't) or the Good Orderly Direction, that we learn in recovery and which is true to our inner selves, are Gods that are both personal and effective for many addicts.

5. Complaining that we cannot use God in our lives because we have no understanding of God would be like saying that we could not use, or rely upon, gravity, electricity or microwaves simply because most of us have very little understanding of them. Indeed, the people who know most about these things would probably emphasise how little they know - yet we all use those powers effectively in our daily lives.

6. Our reluctance to involve ourselves in spiritual matters is understandable when we see some of the things done in the name of orthodox or alternative religious beliefs. But we can't get away from it: we do have spiritual lives. What is hope if not a spiritual value? It is certainly not just an intellectual feature: there are many bright people who nonetheless despair. What are love, honour, innocence or humility? These are spiritual values rather than mere emotional states.

7. We see God in other people when we see their struggles and their courage and, most of all, their enthusiasm (Greek: *en theos*, God within). We find God in ourselves when we strive for the best within ourselves. When we accept responsibility for our own thoughts, feelings, actions and reactions, focusing on what we can do for others rather than take for ourselves, then indeed we are living lives of spiritual value. Saying that we try to do God's work, or to allow God to help us in our lives, is saying no more than that we treasure our spiritual values above all others. God is only a word. Using the word God does not mean that we have lost our marbles or our individuality. Far from it, the moment we appeal to God is precisely when we are restored to sanity and relieved of arrogance and ludicrous pomposity. Asking for God's help is purely a phrase in which we recognise that single-minded determination and willpower didn't work in relieving us of compulsive or addictive behaviour: they made them worse.

8. Seeing a Higher Power in all aspects of our lives, respecting all forms of life and all aspects of the environment, and respecting other people's rights to differ from us, are spiritual values that we come to love as they become progressively more important in our lives. Earning our livings and paying our way, building our careers and nurturing our families are all important but is that all that life is for? What about enjoying life simply as life itself? Just being alive, being involved in life in any way, is privilege enough.

9. Recovery is a gift. We did nothing to deserve it. Very often we did everything we could to turn it away. Yet others reached out to help and heal us. If that isn't evidence of a Higher Power than self at work in our lives - then what is?

10. The HOW of recovery (Honesty, Open-mindedness, Willingness) helps us to give something back to life. Many of us would be dead by now if we had not been led to the Twelve Step programme. Many of our friends are dead. We were no different: just luckier. We owe something to life in return for what we ourselves were given. The very least we can do is to hand on the opportunity that was given to us.

11. An attitude of gratitude is more than saying thank you for what we have been given. It is a deep inner awareness that fills up the previous inner emptiness of addictive disease. When we reach out to help others on an anonymous basis we keep what we give away.

12. Serenity is the knowledge that God is continuing to do for us what we could not do for ourselves. Other people may not understand this but that doesn't matter: we do.

Dying and Living

I'm dying. Of course I am: we all are, just by getting older. I don't know the date of my eventual death, nor the cause, but I am certain to die at some time. I hope that the process of my death will be dignified, as painless as possible, and no great nuisance to others. Beyond that, neither dying nor death itself has any fears.

I have no belief nor hope of a specific after-life: only curiosity. After all, I don't know how I got here, yet here I am, so why should I concern myself with where I am going when this life is over?

Despite all the time and energy that others have given historically, both in metaphysics and in religion, to contemplating - or believing in - an after-life, I see no point in doing so. I have enough to do in focusing upon living my current life to the full. Who cares about death and dying when there is so much living to do!

More importantly, I reject the twin evils of institutionalised Church and State (proclaiming their own righteousness while blackmailing, pontificating, stealing and even murdering) when they belittle and scorn my right to live for myself rather than primarily for them or for others. Only by having a sure sense of self will I ever develop a true awareness of other people's right to have the same. Only by loving myself, and life itself, can I learn to love others and respect their right to their own individuality and, further, their right to disagree with me.

Consideration for others can grow only from consideration for myself. Compassion, tolerance, understanding and acceptance cannot be enforced: their self-enhancing virtues can only be experienced and then shown by example.

My responsibility in this life is to live it: to create and to be kind. That's enough for me to be getting on with.

The Objectivist Oath of Ayn Rand

I swear, by my life and my love of it,
That I will never live for the sake of another man,
Nor ask another man to live for mine.

Death and Life

Our attitude towards death determines our attitude towards life:

If death is obliteration and oblivion, then life is an irrelevance.

If death is a recycling process to start life again in a new body, then life is a drudge.

If death is a transition to a new existence in a new world, then life is just a passing curiosity.

If death leads to a reunion, giving opportunity to restore loss, then life is a cumulative tragedy.

If death leads to eternal joy, with an end to shame and suffering, then life is a pathetic charade and mere preparation.

If death is an exciting leap into new discoveries, then life is also an exciting leap into new discoveries.

Despair and Hope

Despair is a long way further down than depression.

Depression has degrees. Despair is an absolute.

Depression can be used as a psychological game to blackmail others into taking action to "help" us by bailing us out of our difficulties, prescribing drugs that formalise our "sick status", and allowing us to demand sympathy while neglecting our adult responsibilities. Despair is not a game, it has no interest in its effect on other people, and its only concept of quantity is zero: no return, no hope, no further questioning, no point in discussion.

Addicts of any kind don't get better until we despair, until we know that we are totally beaten. We go beyond temporary submission (with the opportunity to fight again another day) into surrender (giving up all prospect of further fight).

Despair is the certain knowledge that all our assets and attributes are useless: they are as ineffective and pathetic as Don Quixote tilting at windmills. We may even be aware that our addictive disease knows our good points (say, our minds, our determination, and our generosity) and turns them to its own advantage (making us argumentative, stubborn and profligate).

When we see that all our efforts to get out of the pit simply dig ourselves further into it, we despair.

Hope comes from the recognition that other people like us have also despaired, yet not only survived but flourished in a new life. Maybe all the externals of their lives are exactly the same as before - but the internals are different. In place of self-obsession are self-awareness and self-esteem, evident most of all when they discard their preoccupations and reach out to help others.

We discover from them the essential paradoxes of recovery. If we want hope we have first to despair. If we want to keep our sense of hope we have to give it away to others.

Love

Love is a generous sharing of spirits, caring for myself and for someone else, or for many others, in the same way and to the same extent.

Love is an approach to life, rather than an event: love comes from being loving.

Love builds on experience, growing each day in direct response to consideration for others and in proportion to the work put into it.

Love survives and thrives while mere infatuation withers.

Love and hate are two faces of the same emotion: apathy is the opposite of both.

Love knows when and how to say no.

Love that is unconditional has also to be coupled with firm guidelines on unacceptable behaviour. It is possible to love the person but not his or her behaviour.

Love does count the cost and knows what it is worth paying.

Love is expressed through body and mind: it is not a product of their activity.

Love is fair: take away my possessions, strip me of my dignity, undermine my confidence, criticize me and vilify me, do what you will - but you will never understand love and it will never be yours. It's mine.

Values

I value most:

1. The lives of my wife and children: they represent my primary choices and responsibilities.

2. My own life: I owe it to no one.

3. My principles by which I live my daily life: I do not borrow them from other people. I choose them. I would betray them under duress to save my own life and those of my wife and children but only if no innocent person's life would be lost in the process. I value my life and therefore I value yours.

4. My mind: I do things to enhance it and I don't do things that would damage it.

5. My health: I do things to enhance it and I don't do things that would damage it.

6. My creativity: my creative output confirms that I am alive.

7. My time: I choose what I do with my life each day.

8. My interests: I have the right to my own enthusiasms.

9. My profession: I have a professional responsibility to those who pay for my services in any sphere of my activity.

10. My friends (including some members of my family): my friends share my values. I develop new friendships as I myself change.

11. My possessions: I am entitled to the product of my labours.

12. My country: I would fight to protect our common culture of tolerance.

These are important values to me. What values are important to you?

I value least:

13. My reputation: I judge myself by my own values.

14. My knowledge: I have more to learn.

15. My achievements: some of them were fine - but they are past.

16. My seniority: respect should depend upon behaviour, not upon age or length of tenure of a position.

17. My status: I have none. Therefore I have nothing to lose. My talents, such as they are, go wherever I go. I alone am responsible for the flowering of my natural ability. No other person, and no social position, can give me a sense of personal value.

18. My physical prowess: this would be a ludicrous value.

19. My "cool": individuality has substance - fashion has none.

20. My professional group: those I respect are counterbalanced by those I do not, as in any other profession. I set no store by my particular profession: take away my daily enjoyment in my work and I would find another profession.

21. My political group: I have ideas of my own and do not accept that might is right. Mere numbers may produce no more than the lowest common denominator. There are, in any case, more constructive occupations than scoring points off opponents.

22. My financial group: my values are determined by what I believe, not by what I purchase.

23. My family as such: I feel no obligation of family ties to those with whom I share few values.

24. Life after death: I'm too busy and happy in this one.

These are not important values to me. What values are not important to you?

Good

The part of me that resembles

> The child, eager to learn and to explore.
> The elderly person, with a lifetime of experience, who is still enthusiastic and eager to learn even more.
> The expert who knows that he or she knows little.
> The friend who is kind for no other reason than simply to be kind.
> The opponent who respects while challenging.
> The parent who knows that accidents and failures are of no significance.
> The professional who encourages the amateur.
> The critic who genuinely seeks to enhance rather than destroy.
> The humorist with no malice.
> The believer who acknowledges other beliefs.

Evil

The part of me that resembles

The politician, lacking principle and conviction, who takes credit for the ideas and enterprise of other people.

The teacher who undermines spontaneity and self confidence.

The doctor who prescribes without respect for the self-healing powers of body and mind.

The carer who cares more for self than for others.

The parent who exposes a child to cynicism and sarcasm and who is too preoccupied to give time to the child's interests.

The therapist who is utterly convinced of the virtue of his or her own perspectives and techniques but who has little knowledge or experience of others.

The writer or broadcaster who uses his or her skills and influence carelessly.

The corrupt or merely self-satisfied lawyer who has forgotten the concept of justice.

The fighter who oppresses rather than defends.

The banker who is motivated by greed rather than creativity.

Feelings

1. We choose our values in life. Our feelings tell us whether our own or someone else's behaviour is in harmony or discord with those values. When any feeling arises we have the choice to accept it, and the behaviour that led to it, as being appropriate to our values, or to change it by changing our values. Thus, we choose our feelings and our behaviour: nothing and nobody else causes them.

2. Feelings are not a command to action: we can choose to sit with them.

3. Adolescence is the time when we learn, through happy or painful experience, to establish our own value system. By suppressing our natural feelings through the use of mood-altering substances, behaviours or relationships, we fail to learn appropriately from our experiences. We don't grow up.

4. In trying to suppress bad feelings we also suppress the good ones: we become insensitive. Ultimately, we are left with the only pseudo-feelings our addictive disease permits: self-pity and blame.

5. In recovery we rejoice in our capacity to feel the full range of our feelings: the bad as well as the good. They tell us we are alive.

6. Just as other people's actions cannot be held responsible for our feelings and subsequent actions (we have choices), neither can we be held responsible for the feelings and actions of others (they have choices).

7. Events in childhood will create a tape-recording whose emotional and intellectual

components will depend upon our capacity at the time of those events. Thus, the tape-recording will be largely emotional in early childhood and have an increasing intellectual component as we get older. These tape recordings will replay when a current event echoes a childhood event. The emotional and intellectual components will replay in the same relative intensity as when they were first recorded. Thus, an adult event that has echoes of an early childhood experience will set off intense feelings, whereas one that has echoes of a later experience will be more accessible to our intellects and therefore more readily understood and accepted. Some of us may therefore have intense "abuse", "abandonment", "frustration" or other tapes that can suddenly replay in our adult lives. We cannot modify these tapes but we can learn to recognise them and then defuse the perceived need to act upon them.

8. If we look at childhood experience too early in our own recovery, we will tend to get stuck in self-pity and blame, taking our parents' and other people's inventories at the very time when we most need to be taking our own. Some therapists, and even some Anonymous Fellowships, become transiently popular by focusing upon childhood issues and taking parents' and other people's inventories, even while saying that they are not doing so. Far from healing, this causes further damage by refuelling our addictive disease with its vital nutrients: self-pity and blame.

9. The time to look back at childhood experiences is when we can do so with understanding and acceptance of ourselves and of the other people involved (they may have been addicts too) and even reflect with wry humour.

10. Some events in early childhood may have been so traumatic that they fill us with fear, or infuse us with shame, so that they become blocks to our own recovery. When therapists or Fellowships wade into these experiences, in the belief that "they have to be dealt with", they may cause further trauma. When doctors prescribe drugs to suppress feelings they cause even greater damage and simply delay the opportunity for their patients to grow and learn to take responsibility for themselves. One of the principal purposes of residential treatment centres is to provide a safe environment in which patients can recognise what they have in common with others, both in past experience and in distorted perception, so that they can come to terms with their past, however savage it may have been, and learn to make positive healing choices in their own thoughts, feelings and behaviour in future.

11. A necessary part of early recovery is that we need to go through our delayed adolescence, feeling the pain that we deferred or tried to avoid. Taking our own inventory, and working the Twelve Steps to recovery, involve feeling the full range of our feelings, the joys and the sorrows. Again, it helps to do this process alongside others so that we confront the isolation of addictive disease, see our own denial reflected in that of others, and gain understanding, support and challenge from each other.

12. In particular, we learn our differences as well as our similarities. For example, each of us has our own response to fear or anger in other people or in ourselves. That's

the way we are made. We learn that other people do not necessarily have the same responses and we come to accept ourselves as we are. However, all addicts know how to build a small episode of justifiable anger or sorrow into long-term resentment and self-pity that enables us to justify to ourselves (and to other gullible people) that our continued use of addictive substances, processes and relationships is reasonable.

13. We learn to differentiate guilt from shame. Guilt is over what we have done. It is treated in Step IX by making appropriate amends. Shame is over who we are, as addicts. This is treated in Step I, recognising that our addictive disease makes us powerless over being addicts, even while we are still responsible for our behaviour as it affects other people.

14. Grief is the central process of Step I. In acknowledging our powerlessness over particular substances, behaviours and relationships, we lose what have become our closest 'friends'. We grieve over the loss of the good feelings these used to provide us with, even while we try to cast a blind eye over the damage that came with them. Any grief reaction takes two years (Step I therefore actually takes two years in the process of going from initial submission to ultimate surrender) and follows the same characteristic pathway of denial, followed by anger towards anyone and everyone, followed then by depression as the anger turns inwards, then by bargaining as we negotiate our recovery and hope that we can still get away with some addictive behaviour, and finally by acceptance when we know absolutely that we can't. This whole process has to be repeated with each addictive substance, behaviour or relationship so the sensible thing to do is to tackle all addictive outlets all at once right at the start, go through just one grief reaction, and look forward to a life that will variously be happy or sad according to circumstances but in which our feelings will be appropriate and very much our own.

Abuse and Abandonment

1. Everyone on earth has been abused and abandoned in some way. Addicts have no monopoly on these experiences. Further, these events did not cause our addiction, however much we may like to believe so in order to have someone to blame for our present condition. There are vast numbers of people who have been abused and abandoned, perhaps far worse than we have, yet they have not become addicts.

2. Those who have suffered severe abuse and abandonment deserve our sympathy, understanding and support, be they addicts or not. The concept of severity has no absolute scale and, to some degree, the suffering varies with the capacity of the recipient to endure. Some people may have suffered relatively little on an absolute scale yet have been crippled by their own reactions. They are no less deserving of our sympathy, understanding and support. Theirs is a different type of problem from the suffering of those with severe trauma but it is trauma nonetheless and can be just as debilitating. To tell them to pull themselves out of it is comparable to

telling a sufferer from alcoholism to sober up: it misunderstands the nature of the problem and hence the necessary change of perspective for an appropriate solution.

3. Even so, the addict's propensity for blame and self-pity can very easily point one finger outwards at every possible external cause of his or her own problems in life without realising that three other fingers are pointing back at self.

4. There is a further tragedy that sometimes befalls those who have been abused and abandoned: they may be re-traumatised by counselling. Indeed, false-memory syndrome, in which the process of counselling implants ideas and convictions into the patient's head, can be just as damaging as genuine abuse and abandonment. In each case there may be intense psychological and social repercussions that can be extremely traumatic - while the counsellor preens himself or herself on a good piece of work simply because the poor patient was reduced to a gibbering - and pathetically grateful - wreck. That form of counselling (often involving beating cushions and screaming) is definite abuse and abandonment.

5. The appropriate counselling for the trauma of abuse and abandonment, at whatever level of severity or perception, is:

   i.   to acknowledge that the suffering exists and to hear the story of its origin;
   ii. to allow other members of the group to share their own comparable experiences and feelings. Doing this work on a one-to-one basis risks forming a dependency relationship that can be just as damaging and disempowering as the initial trauma. Group support is a dependable resource when appropriately supervised by a responsible counsellor. Groups, when left to themselves, as can happen when the members of the Anonymous Fellowships decide to do "workshops" on abuse and abandonment, can become just as destructive as when they are in the hands of self-seeking counsellors or, worse, self-styled "therapists" or "psychotherapists";
   iii. to help the sufferer to acknowledge that the abuse and abandonment were wrong and an infringement of personal rights rather than something contributed to or even created by the recipient;
   iv. to remind the sufferer of his or her own positive resources, both internal and external, focusing attention towards gentle solutions rather than staying stuck in the problems.

Damage

1. Our addictive disease would like us to focus our attention on the amount of damage other people have done to us. In recovery we need to acknowledge the amount of damage we have done to other people and to ourselves.

2. Initially, however, we do need to look at the damage done to us so that:
   i.   we confirm to ourselves that it did happen and that it was unacceptable;

ii.   we resolve not to allow it to happen again: we develop self-respect;

iii. we endeavour to diminish its effects by consigning it to history, refusing to let it tarnish today. We learn to forgive, or, at least, we let go of the continuing resentment that only damages ourselves;

iv.   we ensure that the principal lesson that we gain from the experience is that we ourselves will be determined to treat other people better than we were treated.

3. When we turn to look at the damage that we ourselves have caused to other people, we may initially be tempted to minimise or justify it by comparing what we have done with what was done to us. This comparison is irrelevant.

4. Physical damage is often the easiest to acknowledge and the easiest to justify to ourselves. We may believe we always had provocation or some other good reason. We need to come to terms with the fact that, whatever the provocation, there could never be justification, particularly not in our behaviour towards children. We are as much responsible for our reactions as for our actions.

5. Sexual abuse of others, particularly of children, is desperately difficult to acknowledge. We think of sexual abuse as something done in hatred rather than love, yet the recipient may be equally damaged by both. Any activity that crosses the normally understood boundaries in a relationship is abusive. Rationalising it by saying that it was enjoyable to both parties is unacceptable, particularly where children are involved. Of course sex is enjoyable - but that is precisely why the experience should be one of choice and preserved for relationships in which sexual contact is appropriate. To justify it even further by saying that we ourselves were seduced (even by children) is the ultimate attempt to wriggle out of accepting responsibility for our own behaviour. Children need to be helped to learn appropriate behaviour from adults. Frequently, abused children, and even adults, may come to blame themselves for abuse done to them - and that compounds the damage.

6. Emotional damage is fearful indeed, particularly in its long-term consequences. An atmosphere of cynicism, sarcasm, distrust, deceit and perpetual criticism sears into the soul. Getting rid of these dreadfully damaging defects of character involves us in becoming aware of what we have done or continue to do. This may sometimes be difficult in a social culture in politics and the media when, in parliamentary "debate" and in some "humorous" television shows, the prime purpose appears to be to denigrate and humiliate. We need to establish our own values in our behaviour towards other people, irrespective of what they may do to us and irrespective of our social culture. We are responsible for our own behaviour, whatever our environment.

7. Mental damage is perhaps the most pernicious of all. Damage the body and it has a good chance of recovery. Damage the mind and it may never get better. A poisonous idea, such as that we owe ultimate allegiance to the institutions of Church or state rather than to ourselves in cherishing our own lives, can inflict the most terrible damage. A human being who discredits or even despises himself or herself is capable of the most fearful acts towards other people. One who values his or her own independence of spirit will also value this in others.

Life is a Journey

The specific events of our lives are not as significant as our progressive capacity to learn from them.

Our ideas may be wrong but they give us inspiration and direction from which to develop better ideas.

We should indeed defend our beliefs but take care that our defences are not the walls of a dungeon, keeping us trapped and out of reach of new light.

We learn most when considering precisely where we may be wrong.

When one of our ideas is proved wrong we should rejoice that a new growing point has appeared.

We are more likely to learn from opponents than sycophants.

Popular acclaim is risky, more likely to lead to stagnation and decline than individuality and creativity.

Although occasional support and encouragement are refreshing, ultimately our individual journeys are exclusively our own.

There is no better goal than to be happy to be alive each day, full of wonder, enthusiasm and gratitude for further opportunity to grow.

Looking Back

Looking back in anger or regret simply brings the pain and sadness of yesterday into today.

We may have been abused and abandoned: perhaps it did happen and it was wrong - but that was then, not now, and it is time to move on.

Childhood experiences made us what we were. Our self-motivated present and future adult experiences have the power to make us what we want to be from now on.

We can stay stuck in the past if we wish to do so, either resenting it or revering it, but that does terrible damage to today.

Learning from our own mistakes is more productive than perpetually reminding ourselves of the mistakes of others.

When we look back with understanding and forgiveness of others we have a better chance of understanding and forgiving ourselves.

There is no misery or preoccupation so intense that one-to-one therapy does not have the power to make it worse.

Seeing the mountains we have already climbed gives us the courage and confidence to climb the next.

Self-Esteem

1. Self-esteem can never be improved by achievement, association or comparison.

   i.   Whatever our achievements, a battered self-esteem will clamour for more.
   ii.   With whoever or whatever we associate ourselves, the glamour will not rub off on to us. Far from it: it will increase our sense of worthlessness.
   iii. Comparisons with other people, making out to ourselves that we are in some way better than they are, give the least secure foundation of all. There may indeed be people who are "worse" than us in some respects but there will also be those who are "better".

2. Self-confidence, and a healthy self-esteem, come precisely when we do not compare ourselves with others.

   i.   Our achievements are our own. Our paintings were ours even though we "can't" paint. Our academic achievements were no less and no more than just that. Our friendship, professional work and parenting cannot possibly have been perfect - but were they good enough? If we did our best, and at least aimed for the stars, then who would criticise us - other than ourselves?
   ii.   Hoping that we can borrow a good feeling from someone else is pitiful. Counsellors of the guru persuasion who encourage us not to "give away our power", or some such twaddle, are making the opposite mistake. We can neither take good feelings from other people nor lose them to them. Nobody and no event can make us feel anything: our feelings are exclusively our own and illustrate that if we have no clear values and principles then small wonder that we try to pinch them from others or fear losing our power.
   iii. The only comparison worth having is the knowledge that there is always something that we can learn from anybody.

3. Self-esteem comes from within. Whatever dreadful things we may have done in the past, we can make amends for them. Even if the person we have harmed is dead, we can do something for a cause he or she would have appreciated. Whatever shame we may have felt about ourselves in the past, we don't have to feel it today. By living a new life, one day at a time, we can build new relationships based on mutual acceptance and appreciation. On our present behaviour we can build new self-esteem.

Safety

1. Sufferers from addictive disease tend to be obsessively concerned for our own safety. This is ironic, considering the risks that we have taken and the lack of concern that we tended to show for the safety of other people. But that's the way it is: we're frightened.

2. This fear is derived from our internal confusion over the Jekyll and Hyde parts of our nature: the addict and the normal human being. Addictive disease lives inside us. Sometimes we fight it, sometimes we obey it. We ask for help to relieve us from it – and then turn the help away. Small wonder that we need a place of safety – from ourselves. But where could we find it?

3. When asking for professional help, we search for someone who truly understands us. At the same time our addictive disease searches for someone who truly understands and accepts it. We (both) find a guru. The human being finds someone who is knowledgeable but the disease is attracted by that same person's belief that addicts can be helped single-handedly. While the human being longs to be understood by someone who will listen endlessly to our tales of woe, our addictive disease is only too happy to see and hear us wallow in self-pity and blame. When the guru nods with condescension (disguised as empathy) the addictive disease nods with satisfaction at one more lost soul – or, with any luck, two.

4. The only safety is in numbers: in a group of recovering addicts. There may be some who are scarcely stronger in recovery than we are – or even less. There may be others who are distinctly strange. Yet overall the average strength of recovery, and of understanding what it takes to separate Dr Jekyll from Mr Hyde, is greater than ours. We can use the strength of the group to reassure us, educate us and even inspire us. The group (as a form of Higher Power than self) can do for us what we could not do for ourselves.

5. To keep that Higher Power, that sense (and reality) of safety, we need to keep in touch with the group, taking from it in return for what we give to it.

6. In recovery we learn to beware of substances, processes and relationships that are risky for us and we develop a sense of responsibility for our own physical, emotional and mental safety and a determination to achieve our best potential, whatever our past or present circumstances.

7. If ever we take the safety of our recovery for granted, - and stop going to Fellowship Meetings and working the Twelve Steps and applying the principles of recovery in all our affairs – then one day we may be surprised to find that we no longer have it. To obtain continuing safety we have to work continually for it.

Trust, Risk and Share

1. When we are first introduced to a therapeutic group of any kind in a treatment centre or in an Anonymous Fellowship, we are encouraged to trust, risk and share. But how can we do that when we are frightened even of opening our mouths? We are dumbfounded by guilt and shame. We are stripped of all our normal securities: our family and friends, our familiar surroundings, and our accustomed way of doing things. We don't know anybody, we don't understand what is going on and we haven't a clue what to say or how to say it. We haven't felt so foolish and ill at ease since experiences of being painfully exposed in one way or another at school. On top of all that we may feel physically awful, mentally blurred and emotionally drained. The one abiding sensation is that we wish we were anywhere other than in a group, with people staring at us and (in therapy groups) with all-powerful counsellors waiting to pounce on hesitations, wrong words, hidden meanings, suppressed feelings and the ever present Catch 22 of denial: acknowledge something and we're trapped, refute it and we're in denial. Surviving our first group is a major achievement!

2. Then something odd happens: we feel closer to the others in the group. Some of the stories we hear are uncannily like our own, not necessarily in the events recounted but in the feelings that accompanied them. When people express their vulnerability we feel drawn towards them, not out of pity but from a sense of being kindred spirits.

3. Reflecting on our own lives, we come to realise how much we have bottled up our feelings and become robotic in our actions. Addictive behaviour has stripped us of our individuality. Seeing other members of the group chip away at the intellectual and emotional shells that imprison them makes us wonder if we could do the same. The more we hear of their hopes and fears, adventures and calamities, joys and sorrows, the closer we get to them.

4. Everyone seems so sophisticated and articulate but we soon discover that some of them have been introduced to the group only just before us. Then a newcomer joins the group and we see our own fears in someone else and we discover, much to our own surprise, that we have already moved ahead, almost by accident. In reaching out to help the newcomer we ourselves get the courage to contribute to the group.

5. In time we discover that the more we put into the group the more we get out of it.

Control and Acceptance

1. We tried control: it didn't work. We tried harder: it still didn't work. We tried it a different way: it seemed to work for a time but then failed again. Addicts, and those who try to help them, know this experience only too well.

2. Bravery is admirable but fighting battles that we shall inevitably lose is just plain stupid. Addictive disease cannot be controlled: it can only be accepted.

3. Paradoxically, as soon as we stop trying to control addictive disease it loses much of its power to hurt us. We discover that it was our own energy that fed it. Far from actually controlling, our attempts to achieve control simply concentrated our attention on the problem and made it less likely that we would discover the true solution: acceptance.

4. When we accept that we are addicts, or that people close to us are addicts, we find that the sky does not fall in on our heads as we had feared. To be sure, we feel overwhelmingly sad but even that feeling is gradually dispelled when we meet addicts who are in recovery. They came from the same desperate and lonely place - but they are not there now.

5. When we get to know recovering addicts better, we find we cannot judge them in the way we used to judge all addicts. Yet their stories show that they had similar experiences to our own or to those of people who are close to us. Through being unable to judge them, because their present behaviour and relationships are what we admire, we begin to see the difference between the person and the disease. From that understanding it is a small step to apply the same principle to ourselves and to those for whom we are concerned.

6. We also come to understand that we could never have begun to treat addiction appropriately until we did accept the reality of the disease. It becomes obvious that no disease can be successfully treated while its existence is still doubted. When we do finally accept that we, or other people, are addicts, then we can get on with working an appropriate Twelve Step programme and we need never look back.

7. Not everything in recovery is a bed of roses. How could it possibly be? Some aspects of our lives inevitably change. Some relationships falter. Some people try to persuade us to go back to the way we were and to the very processes that we know from experience don't work. Some people, perhaps feeling under threat themselves, actually criticise us for our abstinence. We ourselves may well have been free with our own criticism in the past so we can't complain now. All this we simply accept - and get on with living our new lives.

Willpower and Letting Go

1. People (especially addicts themselves) often imagine that all that is necessary to control the use of mood-altering substances is a clear philosophy of life, healthy pursuits and, above all, willpower. The fallacy in this belief can be seen clearly in the non-addictive aspects of the lives of sufferers from addictive disease. Frequently these people are imaginative, creative, productive and highly skilled in many aspects of life until they become involved in the use of mood-altering substances and processes. They may even manage to control their addictive use for some considerable time - at the price of their mood. They may become irritable or morose while being determined to demonstrate to themselves and to others that they are in control.

2. Ironically it is the presence rather than absence of willpower that keeps many of us from seeking and obtaining the help we so desperately need. The more we focus our determination on proving that we do not have a problem, the longer it takes us to come to terms with the fact that we do.

3. Some sufferers go to their deaths in their determination to exert their willpower. Confusing it with free will, they talk of their rights when all that was at stake was their self-will and pride.

4. Letting go of the burden of self is the basis of Step III of the Anonymous Fellowships, in which we come to recognise that we need a higher power than self to help us with our addictive or compulsive behaviour. Indeed, if we could control it on our own (and be comfortable doing so, rather than stuck in the desperate "dry drunk" state in which our mood and behaviour are so awful that we might just as well be drunk or using other mood-altering substances or processes) then it wouldn't be an addiction or compulsion in the first place.

5. The burden of self is the stubbornness that insists we must be right. This has nothing to do with fighting for causes in which we believe. It has everything to do with belligerence, fighting anything and everything that gets in our way, irrespective of the increasing evidence that we are wrong and irrespective of the increasing damage that our wilful behaviour causes to ourselves and to others.

6. In our first contact with the Anonymous Fellowships or with a treatment centre we may be like wrestlers who are prepared to submit and accept defeat in a particular bout - but still hope to get back into the ring at a later date. When we finally let go we surrender and have no wish to fight ever again.

7. Letting go does not mean giving up and becoming pathetic. It is learning that true bravery means knowing when to surrender rather than risk further casualties in a pointless battle in which there can be only one outcome. Letting go means relinquishing our determination to prove ourselves right in all sorts of battles and then turning our energy towards something more worthwhile.

8. Our fear of letting go is that we will drop into an abyss in which life has no fun or purpose. The paradox is that only by taking this risk do we discover our true inner strength that comes alive when we forget about ourselves and reach out to help other sufferers. We gain the strength we had sought. We keep it by giving it away. We get far more fun, and a far deeper sense of purpose, than we ever had.

9. In recovery we use our determination and willpower in our professional work and other appropriate outlets and, in particular, in making sure that we are absolutely and totally determined to go to regular meetings of the Anonymous Fellowships and to work the Twelve Step programme of recovery each and every day.

Anger, Resentment and Forgiveness

1. Anger is a normal human feeling when something conflicts with our values. "Using" addicts have such bizarre values that almost anything conflicts with them and we become permanently and obsessively angry. When the anger turns in on ourselves we become even more depressed than we already were.

2. Anger may on occasions be appropriate. However, allowing it to fester and become a continuing resentment gives it headroom, sometimes for many years, and this causes us far more damage than the original irritant.

3. The Big Book of Alcoholics Anonymous rightly terms resentment as "the number one offender". Once it takes hold, it seeps into every aspect of our lives and destroys us from within.

4. When we make a list of those we have harmed there are some names we find difficult to put down because we feel that primarily these people owe us amends for what they have done to us. That is not the point. If we are to rid ourselves of our resentments (for our own benefit) we need to make our amends with a good grace to those we have harmed, irrespective of whatever they may have done to us.

5. As we progress further in our recovery we find that we become generally less angry. Often we recognise our own former intolerant behaviour in other people. We don't accept the behaviour but we react more with understanding than anger.

6. When eventually we look back appropriately at the events of our childhood we need to do so with consideration for the adults around us at that time. This is impossible in early recovery because we are so suffused with resentment that we see only what was done to us, not the problems and perspectives (or even the addictive disease) of those who helped or hurt us. Our resentments lose their power when, eventually, we see the reasons why people behaved towards us as they did. That is not to say that what was done to us was right. Rather it means that we do not need to carry the damage any more as a continuing resentment.

7. The reason why in early recovery we should not look too deeply into childhood events is that we need to focus at that time on taking our own inventory. Far from trying to justify our behaviour, we need to examine it dispassionately and accept the harm that we have done to ourselves and to others. We can take other people's inventories when we are ready to do so (probably not before we are about six years into recovery) with understanding, forgiveness and even with humour.

8. As recovery becomes more established we find that our understanding of human frailty - both our own and other people's – deepens, and we have progressively less to be angry about.

Making Decisions

1. We make some crazy decisions at times. Looking back, we wonder how on earth we could have been so stupid as to make some of our previous decisions and act upon them in the way that we did. We need to understand that at all times we do the things that seem to be most sensible at the time or, at least, better than what we perceive the alternatives to be.

   i. Sometimes there was no viable alternative: we knew that what we were choosing to do was less than perfect - but the other options were worse.
   ii. Sometimes we simply hadn't at the time seen a possibility that occurred to us later.
   iii. Sometimes we were so frightened that we took immediate action without considering long-term consequences.
   iv. Sometimes we were caught between conflicting interests.
   v. Sometimes we were driven by internal or external forces greater than our capacity to resist.

   It is easy to criticise ourselves when we look back. It is healthier to give ourselves the benefit of the doubt, as we usually would to anyone else, when we question our previous motives and sanity.

2. If the alternative was to commit suicide, then the decision to use mood-altering substances, processes and relationships was a sensible option because that saved our lives. In time, when the damage from addictive use mounts up, the decision becomes progressively less sensible. At this point we try to persuade ourselves, and other people try to persuade us, simply to make a decision to stop. Then we find that we can't - or, more precisely, we can stop for a time but then we go back to our addictive behaviour. Then we get really frightened. This is the crucial step that non-addicts can never understand. In other aspects of life we are perfectly capable of making sensible decisions - but here we are hooked. If we weren't hooked, it wouldn't be addiction.

3. Paradoxically, we gain the strength to make appropriate decisions at the precise moment when we abandon all hope of being able to do so by ourselves. It is this miracle that lies at the heart of recovery in the Anonymous Fellowships. By making the simple decision to go to regular meetings of the Anonymous Fellowships and work the Twelve Step programme on a continuing basis, the clouds of confusion and despair are lifted and we can make any decision we want.

Judgement

1. We all make judgements and so we should. We judge in accordance with our values. If we have no clear principles and values then we are indeed in a sorry state. If we allow others, such as the Church or State, to dictate our principles and values then we are in an even worse position: as fodder for cannons and heaven knows what else.

2. To be judgemental is altogether another matter. In this, we sit in judgement upon others, criticising and blaming them. Addicts have post-graduate degrees in judgementalism: nothing is right; nobody understands; anybody and everybody else is at fault and they are the cause of our problems.

3. In recovery we need to reclaim our capacity to make balanced judgements:

i. How much of our behaviour is a chosen response to our various environments and how much goes with us wherever we go?

ii. What aspects of our lives are perfectly capable of being within our control and what are not and never can be?

iii. Which activities are beneficial to us and which are harmful?

iv. Which relationships are beneficial to us and which are harmful?

v. Where have we failed or succeeded in drawing appropriate boundaries?

vi. What aspects of our lives have we neglected and what have we done to excess?

vii. What is worthy or unworthy of our time?

viii. What is important and what is not?

ix. Who is important to us and why?

x. What do we understand of having enough, doing enough or being good enough?

xi. On what do we base our self-esteem?

xii. What are our real enthusiasms and how well do we nurture them?

xiii. What gives us lasting pleasure and what is merely transient?

xiv. What is likely to be of benefit or harm and what is not?

xv. Where is our balance in physical, emotional, mental and spiritual aspects of life?

xvi. What is a balanced life?

xvii. What do we give to the world in return for what we take from it?

xviii. How do we interpret honesty, open-mindedness and willingness?

xix. How far have we moved from blame and self-pity towards acceptance and gratitude?

xx. What is the significance of working a Twelve Step programme in our lives?

Barriers and Boundaries

1. When the shutters come down there is no way in. That is the simple truth about addiction: once the addict's mind turns towards using addictive substances, processes or relationships, there is no way past that impenetrable barrier. The most extraordinary clinical experience is actually seeing the shutters come down. One moment we may be talking to someone we know as a human being and then something is triggered in his or her mind, the spiritual shutters come down, there is no mental or emotional entry, and that's that - the addictive disease is in charge and the human being is no longer available.

2. The important realisation is that the shutters come down before the addict takes a drink or a drug or has a binge or whatever. The mind is turned off, the lights go out, and a drink, drug, binge or whatever becomes almost inevitable. This is an entirely

different experience from trying to get through to someone who is already drunk, drugged, pigged out or whatever. In that case one is observing the effects of these substances or processes as they would occur in any human brain. Seeing the shutters come down in advance of the use of a mood-altering substance or process is an experience visible only in addicts. It emphasises that addictive disease precedes the use of mood-altering substances, processes and relationships and is not a consequence of their use. We do not become addicted: we are born addictive.

3. When someone else's shutters are down we simply have to wait until they rise again. They will not do so again that day and may not do so until after a binge. When they do rise again, the window of opportunity for access to the human being may be small. Opportunities for intervention have to be taken when they arise and always before any use in that day of any mood-altering substance, process or relationship.

4. When we are in the grip of our own addictive disease, when our shutters are down, we lose all sense of appropriate boundaries in our behaviour and relationships. The disease is in the driving seat and it takes us where it will. This is not to say that we are not responsible for our behaviour towards other people. Even though we may be in a blackout and subsequently genuinely cannot remember our actions, the responsibility is still ours and ours alone when our behaviour affects other people. While we are conscious and can still walk and talk we are still making choices and are therefore responsible for the consequences of those choices. For example, our addictive disease drives us towards using mood-altering substances and processes but it is still our choice to drive a car or to be violent. It is often said that it is even our choice to use mood-altering substances, processes and relationships in the first place. When the only perceived alternative is suicide it is a sensible choice. Even if we ourselves argue that our behaviour was not in conscious control, we should still be held accountable for it. Not only is that essential for social cohesion, it is also a necessary factor in guiding us towards recovery: as addicts we contemplate changing our behaviour only when the prospect of continuing as we are is perceived to be more painful than the prospect of change.

5. In recovery we learn to establish appropriate boundaries, being totally responsible for ourselves and ensuring that we neither impose upon other people nor allow them to impose upon us. Through the Twelve Steps, we work actively to put our addictive disease into remission so that the shutters stay up and the human being remains in charge.

Rejection

1. Being rejected on occasions is a fact of life. We have to learn to accept it and let the experience go, rather than allow it to fester.

2. Frequently a better opportunity presents itself once we truly let go of the former rejections.

3. Sometimes our talents are not appreciated because other people do not share our values, experiences or perspectives. We might have rejected their talents for the same reasons. We lose nothing by the rejection. We retain our individuality.

4. Men and women who have something original to say inevitably pose a threat to the complacency of those who do not.

5. As Professor Friedrich Hayek said in his eighties, "Never try to influence your contemporaries; wait for them to die off."

6. We can tell the quality of a man's or woman's ideas and personal philosophy by observing who accepts or rejects them.

7. Committees exist in order to avoid the commitment and responsibility of making individual judgement. They achieve the lowest common denominator. It is no disgrace to be rejected by a committee.

8. To be popular we may need to say what people want to hear - but what a terrible price to pay in loss of our own integrity!

9. If we are rejected in a personal relationship:

    i.   the other person may have another close relationship with more in common than with us: the degree of mutuality is what defines any relationship;
    ii. we may need to examine our own behaviour and consider whether it might be unacceptable to anyone or even everyone;
    iii. we may simply have been seeking a close relationship in order to feel better about ourselves and without serious regard to the wishes of the other person.

10. Using addicts become progressively more isolated, partly because other people reject our behaviour (the exceptions tend to be compulsive helpers who need to be needed either personally or professionally), and partly because we reject other people as we become progressively more blaming and self-pitying, believing that all our problems have outside rather than inside causes.

11. In recovery we learn to accept people as they are and events as they happen. Living one day at a time, we make fewer demands upon other people and we are more tolerant and understanding both of them and of ourselves.

Jealousy and Admiration

1. There can surely be no more stupid an emotion than jealousy.

    i.   If we are jealous of someone's talent we may not be giving credit for the work that has gone into training and practising it.
    ii. If we are jealous of his or her possessions we may not be giving credit for what it took to get them. If they were acquired fortuitously or dishonestly they will give no true pleasure and there is nothing to envy. If they were acquired industriously and honestly then admiration would be more sensible.
    iii. If we are jealous of his or her relationships we should ask ourselves what we have done to damage our own.
    iv. If we are jealous of health and happiness we may be failing to realise that these are often the product of responsible and considerate behaviour rather than mere good fortune.

2. When we are jealous we may make the mistake of comparing how someone else looks with how we feel. For all we know, the assets or attributes that we envy may have brought no happiness at all. They may erode rather than enhance the human spirit.

3. Admiration can be just as easily misplaced as jealousy. When people are worthy of admiration through their actions then to admire them is nothing less than they deserve. However, we should beware of deifying human beings: this risks damaging them (if they buy into it) and us.

4. "Using" addicts tend to be "all or nothing" people. Something or somebody, in our view, is either all bad or all good. This extremism is not only a sign of immature judgement on a particular occasion, it also devalues our opinion on any other issue.

5. In recovery we learn to get rid of every last shred of jealousy. This form of comparison is odious and inappropriate. In its place we make comparisons between what we hear and what we see:

    i.   Do other people "walk the walk" or merely "talk the talk"? Are they true to the acclaim they give themselves? Does this show in their practical achievements (rather than in the froth of public acclaim) and in their relationships?
    ii. Do we ourselves ensure that our own actions speak louder than our words? Do we have something in our lives that other people might want to emulate or admire? If not, why not?

Respect

1. Respect has to be earned. It does not come automatically with a personal, professional, political or even royal position.

2. We tend to respect those who are:

    i.   talented but carry their ability lightly and without pomposity;
    ii. considerate in their behaviour, being thorough, reliable and efficient and having a sound analytical sense;
    iii. creative;
    iv. uncomplaining.

3. "Using" addicts may give lip-service to these characteristics but our behaviour belies our words. We tend to be:

    i.   talented but to have submerged our talents in a mish-mash of preoccupation, confusion and bombast;
    ii. generally inconsiderate, intolerant and arrogant, particularly in the superiority of our knowledge - especially about addiction itself;
    iii. progressively unprofessional, sacrificing self-discipline and judgement to the demands of our addiction;
    iv. creative in our manipulations, rationalisations and self-justifications but producing less and less of any commercial, social or artistic merit;
    v.   blaming and self-pitying and becoming increasingly demanding that other people should accept us as we are, rather than have any expectations of us.

4. Through having little or no respect for ourselves, we reflect this outwards and become very critical and disrespectful of others.

5. Inevitably, when our addictive disease tightens its grip on our behaviour, other people lose their respect for us. Eventually the only people who will tolerate us are other using addicts.

6. In recovery we regenerate our self-respect through:

    i.   reclaiming our talents and recognising that these are gifts that we have a responsibility to nurture and apply;
    ii. being understanding and tolerant of others, sometimes recognising our own former behaviour in them;
    iii. focusing our attention primarily upon our own behaviour;
    iv. fostering our originality and seeing how our experience can benefit others;
    v.   becoming more accepting of the true potential of self and others through being less perfectionist in our demands and less slovenly in our behaviour.
    vi. We have to earn the respect of others.

Courtesy, Kindness and Consideration

1. There is a lot more to courtesy, kindness and consideration than saying thank you, giving presents and being helpful.

   i. **Courtesy is:**
      saying thank you in such a way that the other person knows we really mean it; avoiding cynicism and sarcasm at all times; having a courtesy of the heart; thinking and talking well of other people as the first option; behaving equally sensitively to adults and children, rich and poor, friends and critics; being the first to make an appropriate apology or amends, irrespective of what may have been done to us; replying to letters; getting things done on time, and giving better service than we would expect to receive.

   ii. **Kindness is:**
      giving presents that the other person is likely to want; giving serious consideration to another person's idea even though initially it appears ridiculous; remembering (making notes if necessary) other people's personal details; going out of one's way; giving time and making it appear that one has all the time in the world; taking time and not rushing to conclusions and opinions; doing something before being asked to do it.

   iii. **Consideration is:**
      being helpful in ways that the other person wanted; making the effort to see things from the other person's perspective; considering the differences between another person's experience and capacity and our own; avoiding giving advice unless requested and even then only in general terms and expressly based on one's own experience; choosing to make the effort to improve a relationship.

2. "Using" addicts are generally bad at courtesy, kindness and consideration. We have to learn or re-learn these behavioural characteristics in recovery. If we are to keep our addictive disease in remission, we have to be centred on other people rather than ourselves. We avoid being obsequiously people-pleasing but we remember that being self-centred destroys us.

Patience

1. St Augustine is reputed to have said "Lord make me chaste - but not yet". Correspondingly, using addicts tend to say "I want what I want when I want it and I want it NOW!"

2. Coming into recovery, we tend to want a magic fix, as if recovery were simply another "drug" that would give us something for nothing. We hear the Twelve Promises and expect them to come tumbling out of the sky instead of being

specifically linked to working Step IX. We expect other people to appreciate us and forget all about our previous behaviour simply because we are now abstinent. We want the rewards without the effort - and we want them immediately.

3. The concept of living one day at a time applies not only to learning how to survive addictive cravings or how to live constructively in spite of unsolved problems, but also to allowing recovery and its benefits to come at their own pace. Sometimes we grasp an idea or way of doing something, straight away. At other times it eludes us for ages and we keep getting it wrong. Every time we take a pace forward something else slips out of place and we seem to have taken two paces back.

4. Recovery is not a single event, such as putting down a particular addictive substance, process or relationship: that is mere abstinence. Recovery is a continuing working process. We are standing on an escalator that is for ever moving downwards and we have to step forward actively, using the Twelve Steps, if we are to maintain our abstinence and obtain the full spiritual (i.e. appropriate physical, mental and emotional) benefits of life in recovery.

5. In order to move forwards we have to draw a line across the past. This alone is difficult enough. Our whole tendency is to dig over the past, poisoning the present with resentments, blame, fear, guilt and shame and with memories of damaging events and disturbed relationships. In time - if we give ourselves the time - we come to see that the only valid purposes of looking back into the past are to learn from it, so that we do not repeat those experiences, and come to identify the people we have harmed so that we can subsequently make appropriate amends to them.

6. Looking to the future, we need first to clarify our goals. Instead of rushing in to change various aspects of our lives, we take our time to acknowledge that we ourselves have been the architects of our own misfortunes in the past and that the major changes we now need to make are primarily internal rather than external. Further, the internal changes need to be the focus of our immediate attention; the externals can wait.

7. In order to understand where we have gone wrong, we need to ask ourselves the question "To whom have I been trying to prove what?". Our previous behaviour has been determined by our previous answers to that question. Our future behaviour will be determined by our future answers to that same question. In a bizarre manner we have always got what we wanted. For example, sometimes we wanted the world to see that we were in pain or that we had been unfairly treated. We chose our mood and behaviour in order to obtain the responses that we wanted from other people. It takes a clear head - and therefore a fair amount of time - to be able to understand and accept this concept of individual responsibility for our own thoughts, feelings, actions and reactions. We may demand new insights on a plate (or more commonly demand that our previous insights be proved right all along) - but it doesn't work that way: it takes time.

8. All we can do constructively is to live in today, working the Twelve Steps one at a time in the order in which they were written, working to achieve the best potential within us. If we can do that, just one day at a time, we can relax and we can afford to be patient, knowing that the full rewards of recovery will be ours - in time.

Boredom and Complacency

1. Addicts are the fun people. We always were creative and imaginative and we always will be. We do not have the exclusive claim to originality but people who lack this essential spark will never be addicts: they don't think and feel the way we do and they would never take our risks. They live out their grey, responsible lives from one day, week, month or year to the next without noticeable effect on the advancement of ideas, the welfare of peoples, or the gaiety of nations.

2. Yet, in contemplating recovery, our greatest fear is that we shall come to resemble them. We point to the great creative writers, artists, musicians, playwrights and the like, who were addicts of one kind or another, and we wonder if they could have produced anything worth-while without their use of alcohol, drugs or other mood-altering substances, processes or relationships. We recall our own attempts to give up our own addictive behaviour and we remember the dreadful time we had in thinking clearly and doing anything at all, let alone producing anything original. We had become dependent upon mood-altering substances, processes and relationships in order to be creative. It all comes as part of one package.

3. In recovery we come to see that these observations and concerns were mostly complete rubbish. It is true that addiction leads to "state-dependent learning" i.e. discovering that the only way that we can reproduce an activity accurately is to be in the same (mood-altered) state in which we first learned it. However, the truth is that the great creators we single out became less creative as their addiction took hold. We ourselves had also become progressively less creative. Indeed, we had become hackneyed and monotonous in our lugubrious and morbid descent into the mundane. Our addiction was driving us to become the very things that we had feared, rather than protecting us from them. In fact, nothing on earth is as boring and monotonous as addictive behaviour itself; nothing as unoriginal, nothing so destructive of creativity.

4. Because of "state-dependent learning", many of our skills have, to some extent, to be re-learned in early recovery. It certainly is difficult learning to do things without the various stimuli on which we had become dependent. However, we discovered remarkably quickly, after mere weeks, that our old skills returned and our originality was restored to new heights.

5. But addictive disease hadn't done with us yet: it never gives up. It makes us complacent. We forget the desperate struggles we had to get out of its stranglehold. We return to the beliefs that we are masters of the universe and that we no longer need

to depend upon regular meetings of the Anonymous Fellowships and working the Twelve Steps. They became boring. From that point our future decline is predictable.

6. To remain in recovery, to remain creative, we have to see boredom and complacency for what they are: traps set for us by our addictive disease. Great heavens, are we really so pathetic that we cannot find fascination and even excitement in any situation, especially in the processes that turn round our entire philosophy of life and its practical output? If not, we are not the creative and imaginative artists we thought ourselves to be.

Contentment

1. "Using" addicts have problems with people, places and things: they are never right.

   i. People don't understand us and are insufficiently sympathetic over our difficulties. They are preoccupied with their own concerns and don't care about us. They have privileges and opportunities that were denied to us.
   ii. The places in which we live or work are not suitable for our needs. They don't take account of our particular requirements. They have obvious faults to which nobody has given proper attention.
   iii. Things go wrong, get in the way, are incorrect, could be a great deal better if other people took the trouble to do their jobs properly, were better previously, would have been all right if other people hadn't interfered, and would generally be fine if people had followed our advice or had a fraction of our intelligence.

2. Recovering addicts are grateful for what we've got.

   i. People may not understand us or be sympathetic but why should they? Have we taken the trouble to understand them and their difficulties? Why should they not be preoccupied with their own issues? Have we given them the time and attention to enable us to understand their perspectives? Are we aware of what other people have done to capitalise on their privileges and opportunities? What have we done to capitalise on our own?
   ii. Our needs are remarkably few and we adjust our wants accordingly. Anything over and above our needs is a gift and we adjust our requirements accordingly. If we observe defects in our surroundings, we ask first what we ourselves could do to rectify them.
   iii. In recovery all sorts of things can still go wrong, in the most remarkable ways - almost as if they were doing so specifically in order to test our patience and forbearance. So what? Whoever said that life in recovery would be easy? Events are unimportant: our own actions and reactions are what count. These are what go to make us content with our lives as they are.

3. Ambition is the core of creativity: to do the best we can, to give the most to life and maybe get what we deserve in return, to form close relationships that give mutual warmth and satisfaction.

4. Yet, in recovery, even while we strive we are content. True contentment has little to do with possessions - and the part of pride of posession that is valid has more to do with memories and associations than financial value. Obviously there are circumstances in which it would be difficult or impossible, or even wrong, to be content but even then our actions and reactions make the worst or the best of our lot, whatever it may be.

Failure and Fallibility

1. Charlie Brown pays five cents to Lucy, the psychiatrist, who says "You win some … you lose some". Charlie Brown, who has never won anything in his life, responds, "Oh, that would be wonderful!". Schulz, the creator of the "Peanuts" cartoon strip, makes an enchanting hero out of the permanent failure, Charlie Brown. As Professor Robert Nesbit of M.I.T. points out, this is sound because failure is an everyday occurrence, with which we can all identify, whereas success is rare and transient. Schulz leads the way in helping children to come to terms with failure, as they will surely have to do many times, rather than for ever crave success, which will equally surely disappoint.

2. Failure and success are relative concepts rather than events. They require the performance of other people for comparison. We may fail in a particular contest - each one of us has some things that we are not good at - but did we really fail? Why should it matter that other people are better in that particular respect? Are there no other opportunities for us, even in this particular sphere of life, let alone in others? Does our pleasure and self-image have to depend upon winning, rather than doing as well as we can? If we do win something, does that make us generally better than other people? If we lose, are we worse? What a miserable philosophy it is that seeks success by comparison.

3. Of course we do the best we can; we are right to be proud of specific achievements (such as winning just the occasional game of tennis), but surely the real challenge in life is to be happy and fulfilled, irrespective of worldly trappings and accolades. We need to find our own niche that suits us. Other people may want to be the fastest runner, the highest earner, the elected representative, the prize-winner, but there are other goals (to be kind, to be fair, to be honest, open-minded and willing) that are more rewarding and certainly longer lasting and these are available to anybody.

4. Addicts of all kinds try to compensate for our poor internal self-image by changing our externals: our possessions, our titles and status, our associations with other people or with organisations, our physical shape. But to what end? This is a never-ending quest, doomed to be overtaken by further cravings. The Duchess of Windsor is reputed to have said that it is impossible to be too rich or too thin. She was wrong on both counts.

5. We may seek the perfect partner, the perfect home, the perfect job, the perfect this or that, but in each case we are defining the object by our current perceptions. Have we no ambition to grow and to change? Is our judgement always going to stay the same? What a fearful prison that would be for ourselves and for those around us. In any case, flaws provide originality and may, as in nature, be the stimulus to new development.

6. The quest for excellence is altogether a different thing from the quest for perfection. Excellence is admirable and achievable. It stimulates inspiration and leads to change, the necessities of survival. Perfection would stop us dead in our tracks.

7. "Using" addicts try to make ourselves impervious to criticism. We have such a poor self-image that we become bitterly resentful when other people dent it even further. We then justify our behaviour. We insist that our opinions are absolute truths. We defend the indefensible. We discard relationships that do not work according to our design, with ourselves at the centre. Ultimately we have a social group of one.

8. In recovery we acknowledge our fallibility. Sure, we get things wrong - and we admit that straight away so that one error does not lead to another and then another and then yet another so that we can't remember where all the deceptions, prevarications and rationalisations began. We take our own inventory, rather than those of other people, each day, acknowledging both what we have done well and badly, those we have helped or harmed. Through acknowledging our fallibility we discover new opportunities for growth and can even come to expect miracles.

Independence

1. Independence is difficult for addicts. We know how to be self-centred, singing the song "I, I, I." to the tune of "Me, Me, Me.". We know how to be physiologically and psychologically dependent on various mood-altering substances, processes and relationships. We know how to be self-pitying and blaming. We know how to have great expectations of other people, society in general and the government in particular. We know how to stick to our own perspectives rather than try to see those of other people. But we don't know how to be independent.

2. We ask a counsellor for help and we are given some imbecile notion of having "given our power away", as if we were the ones who had been considerate and sensitive to others. Even our people-pleasing was a form of emotional blackmail. Our emotional dishonesty with ourselves was compounded by the counsellor's intellectual dishonesty, using glib phrases without working out their true meaning and implication. That was fine by us because we were always on the lookout for rationalisation and justification of our behaviour. Conversely, the best help we can ever be given is to be challenged to be independent and responsible, doing the things we need to do on a day-to-day basis in order to get into recovery and stay in it, by becoming a giver rather than a taker. Giving our power away is exactly what we need to do. Relying upon a Higher Power than self is fundamental to recovery.

Developing mutually satisfying and supportive relationships is one of the great benefits that come from putting work into the Twelve Steps rather than expecting results to come from mere recitation. We are helped ourselves when we take our minds off our self-centred needs and demands and reach out to help others.

3. Worst of all, we may have developed a "them" culture, feeling isolated, put upon, or even persecuted. This has a huge constituency. When Elvis Presley sang "Are you lonesome tonight?" all the addicts in the world cried out "Yes!" in unison and he made millions. When other people, even the British Royal Family, are blamed for the self-pitying self-indulgence of an addictive young girl, the pathetic contingency rises as one to claim "Yes, we are martyrs too!"

4. As addicts, our natural selves are malign, just as the natural state of people with short-sight is to have poor vision. Short-sighted people have to accept that specific limitation and learn how to do something about it on a day-to-day basis. Laser surgery to the cornea may nowadays give a permanent cure. As addicts, we have to accept that our natural state is to have a mood disorder. We are not normal people who have suffered: we are by nature abnormal. We have to learn how to do things on a day-to-day basis that enable us to function normally. Pharmaceutical substances, far from giving us independence and normality, simply give us a different form of dependency, with tragic loss of range of normal feeling. Perhaps, some time in the future, genetic engineering will establish "normality" for addicts but how much will we lose in the process? Will we lose our individuality and become emotional clones in a Brave New World? That price is certainly too high when the Twelve Step programme is a perfectly good way of providing normal mental, emotional and practical function on a day-to-day basis, using the homeostatic potential of the brain's own biochemistry.

5. Our pride is all that stands in the way of our becoming truly independent - thinking, feeling, acting and reacting for ourselves. Acknowledging that we are powerless over mood-altering substances, processes and relationships, and that our lives under our own direction have become hopelessly unmanageable, is the first step towards recovery from our dependency. Indeed we do need to change one dependency for another: a destructive one, that totally saps our individuality, for a creative one, that enables us to achieve our best potential. As with wearing glasses for short-sight, we achieve nothing more, through working a Twelve Step programme, than establishing a level playing field alongside other people in the world. Then we have to read the books and do the work, or do whatever else is necessary, with our eyes or with our recovery in order to achieve what we want to achieve.

6. In recovery we learn how to discard the notion of being responsible for other people (except young children) and become responsible to ourselves and to other people in our behaviour. That is what gives us true independence.

Freedom and Responsibility

1. Those who are most vociferous in their demands for freedom are often the first to deny it to others. For example, the demand for freedom to use addictive substances may be coupled with the expectation that someone else will pay for the medical and social consequences.

2. Some freedoms are more appearance than substance. For example, the freedom to dress as we choose is often remarkably restricted by current fashion: the teenager in a suit or dress, or without an ear-ring or nose stud, would be truly free.

3. Some freedoms are coercions in disguise. For example, any form of addiction is in fact a compulsion, the very opposite of freedom. The life of an addict of any kind is singularly lacking in freedom.

4. Genuine freedom has to be universal:

   i.   freedom of religious belief must include the possibility of non-belief;
   ii. freedom of political belief must include peaceful anarchy or libertarianism;
   iii. freedom to do as we please must grant the same freedom to others.

5. Any restriction of freedom must essentially be by consent:

   i. the basis of democracy is fundamentally to take universal power away from leaders, be they kings, politicians, professional bodies, financial magnates or physical brutes;
   ii. an elected committee exists to protect individual freedom, not to force it into submission.

6. The appeal or demand that a professional body, local cabal, or the central government ought to do something is the thin end of the wedge of totalitarianism:

   i.   the belief that other people should do something reduces the sense of individual responsibility to create a free and compassionate society;
   ii. the demand that someone else's freedom should be restricted will be matched by their demands to restrict ours;
   iii. progressive restriction of freedom results in progressive concentration and centralisation of power over individuals;
   iv. central government power is necessary to prevent individuals from wielding power through force of arms. There is therefore a need for an army and a police force but even their membership and funding need to be voluntary and accountable. Beyond that, governmental power tends to be progressively restrictive. As Ayn Rand says, "The difference between a Welfare State and a Totalitarian State is merely a matter of time".

7. The absolute basis of true freedom is the acceptance of responsibility for self and the expectation of other people that they will also be responsible for themselves. Each and every one of us (rather than some corporate body) has a responsibility towards those who are genuinely incapable of taking responsibility. The sheer level of charitable endeavour in our society indicates the wealth of individual compassion and concern and therefore the lack of need for government interference and domination.

8. For addicts of any kind the progressive change in personal philosophy from demanding to contributing, from insisting upon individual pseudo-freedom to accepting genuine individual responsibility, is the cornerstone of recovery.

9. Freedom from addiction restores freedom of choice.

Money

1. Money is itself neutral. How we get it and what we do with it are individual choices and these reflect our personal philosophy.

2. Our attitude towards money indicates our attitude towards ourselves. If we despise money we despise ourselves because we do not respect what it takes to make money. If we respect it we respect ourselves and we spend it wisely.

3. If we earn our money honestly we respect it and ourselves and spending it gives pleasure. If we earn our money dishonestly we despise it and ourselves and spending it gives no true pleasure whatever.

4. Money that is earned through work, or through sensible investment, rightly belongs to its owner. That person deserves respect rather than envy.

5. People who work, or who invest sensibly, are entitled to get money for it. We should not expect other people to do something for nothing.

6. Whatever our needs, we have no right to someone else's money, either directly or indirectly via the government or some other authority.

7. We damage ourselves if we allow ourselves in any way to feel that we have any right whatever to someone else's money. A parent has no moral obligation to bequeath anything at all to his or her children. An employer has no obligation to give anything other than the market wage for the job that he or she created and maintains.

8. We may be given more than we deserve and we should be grateful that someone else is making a gift of the time, skill and effort in his or her life that the money or gift represents. If we expect more, through some curious concept of rights, we are demanding something for nothing - which is as immoral an act as can be imagined.

9. There is no moral obligation on people who have money to spend it in any way other than the way they wish. They deserve thanks if they choose to give it away but they do not deserve criticism if they choose to keep it for themselves. It is theirs, as are their other possessions.

10. People who receive benefit from the state or through charities should remember that the money comes from those who earned it, not from those who confiscated it through taxation or who administer its distribution.

11. "Using" addicts often despise money and themselves. They tend to wallow in self-pity and blame. They often see life as unfair. Some may demand their "rights", expecting others to provide for them. Recovering addicts accept total responsibility for themselves, as a mark of honesty and respect to other people and to themselves.

12. In recovery, through becoming less self-centred and more centred upon other people, we may choose to make financial gifts or to do things that benefit other people. The process of giving is for its own sake and we should beware of two serious potential pitfalls:

    i.   compulsively helping the recipient and thereby encouraging him or her to maintain a physical or emotional dependency;
    ii. becoming pretentious ourselves, believing that we are being saintly rather than simply making a personal choice.

Maturity

Recognising that one has to choose between conflicting philosophies, such as individualism and corporatism or evolution and creation.

Understanding that adulthood is not an automatic accompaniment of parenthood.

Accepting fate without complaint but with every intention of influencing its consequences.

Doing the best we can with what we have.

Acknowledging full responsibility for one's own thoughts, feelings, actions and reactions.

Finding fault with one's own behaviour rather than other people's.

Seeing the best potential in other people and in one's self.

Retaining the innocence and curiosity of childhood.

Believing in one's self, rather than in a guru.

Knowing that mistakes are nothing more than that.

Looking forward rather than backward.

Being willing and eager to learn and grow.

Discriminating between the true and the false.

Confronting evil and actively supporting good.

Fighting for one's beliefs.

Comprehending that status is an irrelevant fraud.

Rejecting the belief that the government ought to do something.

Earning one's own living, if at all possible, rather than accepting (let alone expecting) handouts from other people or the state.

Ignoring opportunities for deception and hurt.

Taking opportunities for honesty and kindness.

Creating opportunities to make amends.

Forgiving.

Sanity

Knowing that cause leads directly or indirectly to effect.

Confronting craziness such as the beliefs that fat comes from something other than food, that one can avoid the physical and emotional consequences of cigarette smoking, that money comes from the money tree rather than having to be earned or sensibly invested, and that one can have illicit relationships or dealings without inevitable ultimate destruction.

Discarding the hocus pocus of mysticism and pseudo-science based upon rigid beliefs rather than statements that can be disproved by better evidence.

Learning from experience and from the understanding that if we keep on doing what we are doing we shall keep on getting what we've got.

Dropping intellectual justifications for unacceptable or inappropriate behaviour.

Getting rid of preoccupations and resentments.

Recognising that other people see us better than we see ourselves.

Acknowledging that enough is enough and that what we want is not necessarily what we need.

Avoiding opportunities for immediate gratification that would lead to longer-term damage.

Moving forwards rather than backwards.

Surrendering when defeat is inevitable.

Reducing our demands and increasing our donations.

Seeing that we damage ourselves each time we damage a relationship with someone else.

Accepting that truth is indivisible.

Staying true to our own principles and beliefs.

Seeing and saying that the emperor has no clothes, whatever it costs to do so.

Saying whatever one is supposed to say, unless others would be damaged, when there is a gun (or its equivalent) pointing at one's head.

Having fun rather than being for ever serious.

Humility.

Hope.

Peace of Mind

Let go of our childhood hurts and injustices.

Accept that life isn't always fair and drop our resentments and jealousies.

Examine our own behaviour rather than other people's.

Stop doing things that damage us.

Avoid self-importance and self-centredness.

Get rid of blame and self-pity.

Take responsibility for our own thoughts, feelings, actions and reactions.

Be healthy in body, mind and spirit.

Be ourselves, not our achievements, associations or comparisons.

Choose to be honest, fair, open-minded, willing, thorough, reliable, sensible, generous, gentle, considerate, respectful and kind.

Meet each day with enthusiasm, spontaneity and creativity, whatever our problems.

Understand the experiences, perceptions and perspectives of others.

Acknowledge and accept our own and other people's mistakes.

Find opportunities to be genuinely helpful to others, respecting their own wishes.

See and know ourselves reflected in our actions and relationships.

Learn equally from success and failure.

Be grateful for the beauty in life.

Look forward in trust and hope as well as with common sense.

Live by our own values in this life, regardless of whatever comes next.

Love the continuing adventure of birth, life and death.

Quality of Life

Examine last year's diary and cheque stubs to see where we spent our time and money. However much we may protest to the contrary, these indicate our actual values in practice. Consider changing them.

Examine our current daily timetable for the entire day and night to see if this is the life we really want and the best life we could have. Consider changing it.

Don't go on doing things we no longer enjoy or never did. Take the risk to change.

Do the things we most want to do.

Don't make a resolution to do something: do it now. This moment is as good as any to begin.

Create things for ourselves, and for our own reasons, in order to illustrate our own beliefs, not those of other people.

Be content with what we have, even while working to improve our lot.

Reject opportunities to cut corners inappropriately: the easy way brings more pain in the long run.

Play to win but accept defeat gracefully.

Be respectful and considerate to critics as well as to friends.

Stay true to one close relationship and concentrate on improving it by focusing on the sensitivities, preferences and needs of the other person as well as our own.

Choose to spend time with the friends and family members whose company we enjoy and whose approach to life we share.

Expect miracles and they will happen because we get ourselves into a position to see them and use them.

Strive to learn.

Wherever possible, live in order to work rather than work in order to live. Never retire: find something else to do.

Find time each and every day for something that is simply fun.

Live within financial means.

Envy nobody.

Get a pet.

Abstinence and Recovery

1. All addicts, of whatever kind, can give up their substances, processes or relationships of addiction for a time. That merely achieves abstinence.

2. Abstinence alone does nothing to take away the inner emptiness that is the driving force of addictive disease - it exacerbates it.

3. Abstinence looks at one or more particular substance, process or relationship of addiction as if they were the cause of all problems and therefore mere abstinence the solution. The truth is that addictive disease goes with the sufferer.

4. Abstinence can persist for some considerable time and even be used as determined "proof" that the sufferer was never an addict in the first place. In this "dry drunk" state (the term used for mere abstinence from the use of a mood-altering substance, behaviour or relationship of addiction but in the absence of full behavioural recovery) the mood and behaviour may be abominable while an air of self-righteous and self-satisfied superiority disguises the inner anguish.

5. Abstinence tends to be admired by other people (including doctors) in the belief that the addict is demonstrating appropriate will-power after all. In time, for the legal substances such as alcohol and sometimes even for cannabis or other drugs, doctors and other people may actually recommend return to "sensible" or "occasional" use. Further, the use of mood-altering prescription medications, such as anti-depressants, may even be actively (and disastrously) encouraged.

6. Abstinence may be used as a weapon by the addict, saying to everyone else "I've done my bit - now you damn well do yours" - and then offloading a range of resentments and unreasonable demands. Often such an addict cross-addicts into another addiction. It is as if each addict has a certain quantity of addiction that has to go somewhere.

7. In recovery we look primarily for peace of mind and happy, mutually-fulfilling relationships and we know that the use of any mood-altering substance, behaviour or relationship can jeopardise that.

8. In recovery we focus on changing our own actions and reactions rather than other people's.

9. In recovery, as time goes by, we work increasingly hard to monitor our progress. We know that our addictive disease never goes away. It needs to be kept in remission through continuing application of the Twelve Step programme in every aspect of our lives.

10. In recovery we know that abstinence from all addictive substances, processes and relationships that affect us will be only the beginning of our spiritual journey. The true purpose of recovery is to enjoy life, use our creativity to the full and get closer to other people.

11. Recovery, the full commitment to working the Twelve Steps as a philosophy for life, may actually be scorned by some other people, particularly doctors and journalists, especially if they themselves suffer from addictive disease. This rejection is of no relevance to us.

12. In recovery we see what we can give to others.

The Family in Early Recovery

1. We did not cause another person's addictive behaviour (except perhaps by giving them our genes), we cannot control it and we cannot cure it. Each addict is responsible for his or her own behaviour. Certainly this is the perspective given to patients in treatment: they need to monitor their own behaviour and not blame anyone else for it. Family members and other close people may sometimes get in the way of that process by taking too much responsibility on to themselves.

2. After years of pain, dashed hopes and disturbed relationships, it is not surprising that family members "walk on eggshells", fearing any possible mistake, when the addict first comes home after treatment. They need to learn not to do this (which is one of the reasons family programmes are so valuable at the time that the addicts are in treatment) and to get on with their own lives irrespective of whatever the addict may do.

3. Family members need to understand that love will not find a way of preventing or treating addictive disease, any more than it would work with appendicitis or short sight. We love anyway. We provide an environment of love and an example of love because we wish to, but not because they have any influence on addictive disease: they don't. They provide the human being with a value to admire, and hopefully emulate, but he or she cannot respond to that while in the grip of addictive disease. Addiction is not simply a bad habit or a cry for help: it is an inner drive that is stronger than anything else, even the love of family and friends or even (especially) the love of self.

4. In early recovery the most important priority for the addict is to get to regular meetings of an appropriate Anonymous Fellowship, preferably to ninety meetings in ninety days. It is this constructive addictive process (reaching out to help other sufferers on an anonymous basis) that takes the place of previous destructive behaviour.

5. Family members and friends may wish to view the process of treatment as comparable to a surgical operation. We may hope that it can be all over and done with so that there can be a return to normal life, with sensible drinking and all the rest of it. Far from it: treatment is more of an educational process and far more painful than any surgical operation, precisely because addicts have to learn to go through it without their customary anaesthetics. It is similar to helping patients with diabetes to learn what they can (and cannot) do in future if they are to get the progression of their disease into continuing remission.

6. Most importantly for family members and friends, we may need to learn again what it is to be family members and friends rather than "doctors" or "counsellors". This may be difficult after years of anxiety but, after all, isn't it ultimately what we most want?

On Leaving PROMIS

Re-entry into the big wide world has a thirty-five per cent relapse rate. You need to be aware of that. These guidelines are written to guide you towards long-term recovery. It is a tragedy when people work so hard for their recovery in PROMIS only to throw it away afterwards.

You have completed treatment at PROMIS, remained abstinent and worked on personal issues. You have developed new understanding of yourself and of your addictive disease. You have made new friends. You may have begun to work on family and other relationships. You have been taught the basic skills of recovery and you have had the opportunity to try some of them in practice.

What you will have learnt is much the same as previous graduates of PROMIS have learnt. Each of you will have worked in group. Each of you will have shared your life story with your peers and received their evaluation on your potential strengths and weaknesses. Each of you will have gained an insight into the powerlessness that you have in your fight against addictive disease. Each of you will have noted the unmanageability of your lives during your determined attempts to control feelings through the use of mood-altering substances and processes. Each of you will have grappled with the concepts of coming to trust a Higher Power than self. Each of you will have made and shared a personal inventory and will have developed a basic familiarity with working all of the Twelve Steps.

There will have been tears and laughter, fear and hope. In your leaving ceremony your counsellors and your peers will have told you their feelings for you and expressed their concerns for you as well as their confidence in your ability to remain in continuing recovery.

Yet one out of every three graduates of PROMIS who have heard, shared and done virtually the same things that you have heard, shared and done, have subsequently relapsed. They have thrown away the opportunities for real happiness and returned to the falsehood and wretchedness of addiction. Despite all the suffering that brought them to PROMIS in the first place, they have gone back to the use of mood-altering substances, processes and relationships in the hope that these would help them to deal with their feelings and cope with the various stresses and strains of their lives. They have hoped that this time, despite previous experience, they would gain the "magic" control that previously eluded them.

The ground is littered with discarded medallions. As the damaging consequences of addictive use (or determined controlled non-use outside the Fellowships) mount up, the level of resentment grows and festers. Even in the Fellowships you may hear cynicism towards ideas and practical suggestions you learn in PROMIS and you will hear justifications of behaviour that is manifestly addictive. You will hear self-pity and blaming. The primary thought processes of addiction are sometimes alive and well and living in the Fellowships! You will be given advice by people whose own lives may have little that is worth copying. You will see cliques and hear gurus.

People outside the Fellowships will "reassure" you that you are so much better now and that you really do not need any of the Twelve Steps or meetings any more: that they have served their purpose. They say that now at last you can return to those who love you and believe in you and you can learn to take life - and mood-altering substances, processes and relationships - "sensibly", just as they can. They may even get angry with you for being "God-struck" and plead with you to get back to your "real" self.

It isn't going to be easy out there, but you can stay in continuing recovery if you are really determined to do so. Being determined to follow these guidelines, whatever may happen, is the appropriate use of will-power. Even in the most unsupportive environments and even when everything in life is coming apart at the seams, you can stay in recovery, and even be grateful for each day, if you are determined to do so. Plenty of other people have done so before you and they often report that their worst day in recovery is better than their best day while using. If that is their experience, it can be yours.

You may need to seek them out and stick with these "winners". They will not be offering an easy path; frequently quite the opposite. They may possibly be flamboyant and have a high profile, but that is unlikely. Most probably they will simply be getting on with life and they will be using the Twelve Steps and regular meetings of the Anonymous Fellowships in order to reach out to others and to apply the Fellowship principles in all their affairs. You can see their recovery in the health of their bodies, minds, feelings and behaviour. They will have an attitude of gratitude and will be honest, open-minded and willing. They will look back to their past with acceptance, understanding, forgiveness and even humour. They will look forward with hope at the same time as keeping their own practical lives in order, one day at a time.

Remember, they came from the same place as you: from the misery and destruction of addiction. Many of them came through PROMIS and fought the same battles that you have fought. Some fought them solely in the Fellowships: it took longer but they got there. Above all, they never believe that recovery is an achievement: it is a continuing process.

It's up to you to decide what you want in the rest of your life. PROMIS has shown you our way and told you what we believe. We can show you our example, but only you can decide what you intend to put into practice on a continuing basis. The choice is yours and so, now, is the responsibility. In this principle PROMIS is like any other educational establishment: we can teach you what we believe would be helpful for you to do - but we can't make you do it. We've done our bit: now it's up to you.

But we don't simply cut you adrift. PROMIS likes to keep in touch, not only through aftercare or out-patient groups but also through the annual reunion and other formal or informal occasions and through individual contacts, by letter or telephone or in person.

These guidelines are written to help to ease the transition back into the "real" world and help you to be prepared for some of the traps that your addictive disease will have ready and waiting for you.

Stay with the programme: it works if you work it. Remember the following basic guidelines:

Basics

1. Stay away from the first use of any mood-altering substances or processes. You know perfectly well what they are: you won't want to debate whether aspirin or rhubarb are addictive. You know they are not, just as you know perfectly well what is. The debate is a smoke screen.

    Look at all your cross-addictions and work progressively to rid yourself of all of them.

    Beware of situations and relationships that could be risky for you.

2. Go regularly to meetings of the Anonymous Fellowships. Initially, ninety meetings in ninety days will provide a firm basis for continuing recovery. In the long term, less than one or two meetings each week is dangerous. What would you be trying to prove? Why would you want to go back to feeling as you did before? What could possibly be more important than continuing recovery from all the torment of addictive disease?

3. Work the Twelve Steps. All of them. We don't get better simply by going to meetings. "**These** are the Steps we **took** ..." is what the Big Book says.

4. Read the literature of the Anonymous Fellowships. Read other recovery texts by all means but beware of anything that even remotely suggests that anyone else had any responsibility for making you an addict or has any responsibility now for your recovery.

5. Get a sponsor in your principal Fellowship. Get a temporary one at first: initial appearances can be deceptive and even destructive.

6. Avoid major changes in your close relationships (other than with using addicts) or in your work or in your domestic arrangements or other significant aspects of your life for at least one year and preferably two. This gives you the time to settle down and other people will have a chance to get used to the "new you". Perhaps they also might change, just as you have changed.

7. Do not, for now, do any more work on childhood issues of abuse or abandonment. They did not cause your addiction. You have done quite enough work on that while you have been in PROMIS. Avoid ACOA (Adult Children of Alcoholics) and CoDA (Co-dependents Anonymous) like the plague. Why would you want to continue focusing on misery? Take your own inventory: not someone else's. Avoid self-pity and blaming.

Recovery has nothing to do with learning how to express anger. As it says in the Big Book of Alcoholics Anonymous, "Resentment is the number one offender."

The time to work on relationships and look back to childhood is when we have been fully in recovery from all our own cross-addictions for a period of at least two - preferably six - years. By that time we can look at other people, even those who have hurt us considerably, with understanding and acceptance, while at the same time developing our own self-understanding and self-acceptance so that we do not tolerate further abuse or abandonment, nor inflict it upon others. Our healthy attitudes and behaviour towards other people, even towards those who have abused or abandoned us, are an exact measure of our own recovery.

8. Avoid antihistamines (prescribed for coughs and colds and allergies), tranquillisers, anti-depressants (including Prozac and similar new drugs) and sleeping tablets. Use pain-killers only on advice from PROMIS, which will generally be that it is safer to use pain-killers appropriately than not at all, but exceedingly dangerous to use them for longer than the few days of acute pain. Relaxation techniques, and increasing the number of Anonymous Fellowship meetings attended, are the best help in any acutely stressful situation.

9. Avoid gurus. Putting faith in one other person, even present or past counsellors of PROMIS, is dangerous. You will pick up that person's blemishes, prejudices and inadequacies as well as his or her good characteristics. Beware of setting up a dependent relationship. Group therapy gives the opportunity to receive broad-based feedback. When giving feedback, avoid giving advice in anything other than general spiritual terms.

10. If, in addition to your primary addictions, you have an addiction to caretaking and self-denial, you will need to look at that behaviour in Helpers Anonymous or other similar "family" Fellowships. Otherwise you will risk "treating" the pain of this aspect of your addictive nature with one or other of your primary addictive substances or processes.

11. Reaching out to help others is not the same as hammering them with proselytising zeal. Share your own experience, strength and hope where appropriate. Then "let go and let God".

12. Stop living off other people or the state. Get a job - even a voluntary one - so that you pay something back to society and to your family and friends after your disease has given them so much grief. Regardless of how other people may have behaved towards you in the past, or continue to behave in the present, see what you can do to benefit others. The beautiful "Promises" outlined in the Big Book of Alcoholics Anonymous come from working Step IX: "Made direct amends to others except when to do so would injure them or others". Remember that.

Working The Twelve Steps

1. The co-founders of Alcoholics Anonymous handed on to us the Twelve Steps as the method that they found worked for them in ridding them of addictive or compulsive behaviour on a continuing daily basis. They said nothing about counselling or therapy or medical care of one kind or another: they had plenty of experience of these treatments but they hadn't worked. They said nothing about delving into early childhood experiences; they examined their own behaviour rather than their parents' and other people's. They said nothing about expressing feelings; they talked only about humility and taking responsibility. The Twelve Steps were based on the personal experience of sufferers, not worked out by well-meaning people who thought they knew what should be good for us.

2. Going to regular meetings of the Anonymous Fellowships gives us the opportunity to counter our "denial", the constant inner urge to persuade ourselves that we are not addicted after all but had just had a bad time or been a bit weak-willed. We also take the chance to reach out to help newcomers and thereby "keep what we give away". We may recite the Serenity Prayer and the Twelve Steps but this is long way from putting them into daily practice.

3. Working the Twelve Steps means exactly that. For each Step in turn we think about it, come to understand the specific challenges that it implies, possibly even write out our conclusions, discuss it with our Fellowship Sponsor or with other members of the Fellowship and then, quite simply and above all, DO IT.

4. The Twelve Steps have been summarised "Trust God; clean house; help others". There is nothing whatever complex about these processes: a child could do them. But adults are more sophisticated: we have to know all the whys and wherefores, we prevaricate and intellectualise and finish up in an analysis paralysis.

5. The word "God", or the concept of a Higher Power, stops many of us dead in our tracks. Yet our daily experience gives many examples of people who have greater knowledge and skills than our own: each of these - and certainly all together - is, or are, a Higher Power. It is also commonplace for us to rely upon the use of processes that we may not fully understand, if at all, such as gravity, radiation, electricity and microwaves. In rejecting the concept of a Deity we may have totally inappropriately elevated our own intellect and understanding into an all-powerful position. We become our own God or Higher Power. Such arrogance is laughable. When we open our eyes we can see miracles: other addicts getting better when all hope was lost. Learning to trust the God or Higher Power of our understanding is no more complex than accepting that we don't know or understand everything and that if something works for others it could work for us and we don't need to fix it or change it in any way.

6. Cleaning house begins with the honest acceptance that our house, our spiritual life with its physical, mental, emotional, social, educational, financial and other

consequences, needs to be cleaned. Thereafter, the process, like any other cleansing, is simply a matter of effort and persistence.

7. Helping others is the necessary act of honourably repaying a debt with gratitude. After all, which of us ever deserved the recovery we were given when others reached out to help us?

Action

1. Father Joseph Martin, the doyen of all addiction counsellors and, together with Mrs Mae Abraham, the creator of Father Martin's Ashley treatment centre in Baltimore, Maryland, USA, says that in recovery "Action" is the magic word. If religious belief alone was sufficient for recovery, then the founders of Alcoholics Anonymous would have stayed in the Oxford Movement and Father Martin would still be drinking. He is right: the Twelve Step programme of recovery has to be worked rather than merely recited.

2. First, we need motivation. No addict will change his or her behaviour until the perceived pain of giving up is less than the perceived pain of continuing as at present. Either the pain in the present has to increase or we may become inspired by a new vision of the future. Either process may tip the balance towards recovery. When other people bail us out of the consequences of our current behaviour, in the mistaken belief that they are encouraging us, we stay stuck. When we see addicts in recovery, and know that they have been where we have been, we become at least curious if not initially enthusiastic.

3. Trying to work everything out in our heads risks creating an analysis paralysis. The centipede, when asked which of its legs it moved first, couldn't move at all.

4. Sitting on the pot of self-pity and blame gets us nowhere other than further into our addiction.

5. Before setting off, we have to have a clear picture of our intended destination. Do we want to give up our addictive substances, processes and relationships or not? Have we had enough pain? Do we still think we can manage our lives our own way? Are other people, places and things still the cause of, or solution to, all our problems? Do we expect to continue doing what we are doing but somehow achieve a different result from before? If we sincerely wish to change, we have to forge an image of what we wish to become. Only then can we set off in the right direction.

6. Following the path that other recovering addicts have already beaten for us is obviously sensible. Otherwise we risk making the same mistakes that others made, sometimes paying a terrible price, even sacrificing their lives. Asking a Fellowship sponsor to guide us is a sensible start.

7.   The example of other recovering addicts encourages us and gives us confidence. If they can work the Twelve Steps of recovery and achieve abstinence, happiness and rewarding relationships, then so can we.

8.   A journey of a thousand miles begins with a single step. The first step of recovery is Step I. Start now.

9.   It doesn't matter if we falter. Of course there will be mishaps - but we have to learn from them so as to keep our heads pointing forwards rather than allowing them to turn us backwards.

10.   As our recovery grows we have to resist the temptation to dig it up to have a look at its roots. Therapy is the last thing we need beyond our initial stabilisation: the Twelve Steps are quite sufficient.

11.   Time is the great healer. The more we work the Steps the more our recovery deepens. If we take our recovery for granted, and stop working the Steps, then inevitably we regress. Our addictive disease stands us on an escalator that is forever moving downwards. We have to step forward just to stay in the same place, let alone to advance.

12.   The more action we take in building our recovery, step by step, being methodical rather than flamboyant, the more secure we become. We need never go back to the spiritual hell from which we emerged. Instead, the prize of spontaneity and creativity - the essence of life itself - is ours.

Spiritual Awakening: Working the Twelve Steps

Multiple addictions have been around probably for ever but certainly since the time of Bill W. and Dr Bob, the co-founders of Alcoholics Anonymous. Bill W. dabbled in the use of L.S.D., may possibly have been a sex and love addict, and died a dreadful death from emphysema, a consequence of lifelong nicotine addiction. Dr Bob also had a dreadful death from the consequence of lifelong nicotine addiction: he died of cancer.

But, leaving aside the possible causes of our eventual death, the use of mood-altering substances, behaviours and relationships and their counterpart, compulsive helping, damage the quality of our lives in the here and now.

Frail though they may have been (we all are), Bill W. and Dr Bob bequeathed to us the Twelve Steps, the fundamental basis of recovery from any or all addiction. Professional therapies and religious beliefs were around before AA, and have been since, and may provide help and support to some, although they may discourage or even damage others. The Twelve Step programme, through being suggested by addicts themselves, and by emphasising that each one of us is free to choose the God or Higher Power (than self) of our own understanding, provides an opportunity for recovery that is not only specifically tailor-made for addictive or compulsive behaviour but is freely available to everyone.

As a medical doctor I am familiar with the standard psychiatric, psychological and pharmaceutical approaches towards treating addictive or compulsive behaviour. From various training courses outside my medical experience, I have some familiarity with Analytical Psychotherapy, Rational Emotive Therapy, Reality Therapy, Control Theory and Choice Theory, Gestalt Therapy, Transactional Analysis, Person-Centred Counselling, Psychosynthesis, Psychodrama and other professional therapeutic approaches that can be helpful to anyone beset with the troubles of life. Any one of these therapies and others can be useful in helping addicts with those aspects of their lives that they share with non-addictive people. Indeed, we use many of these therapies in our work at PROMIS: each member of the counselling staff brings his or her own training, experience, insight and skill. Yet I believe that only the Twelve Step programme tackles addiction at its source.

But if abstinence from alcohol alone was good enough for Bill W. and Dr Bob, why should any of us want more? Surely, those of us who are addictive by nature have to be addicted to something? In answering these questions I can speak only for myself and from my own experience. I want more: I want to be me. I don't want my life to be ruled by addictive cravings of any kind. I want open and loving, rather than manipulative and resentful, relationships. I don't want to be the person I was: I want to be the person I am now, happy and creative despite all sorts of problems in my life.

Professionally, as the director of PROMIS, I want to do whatever I can to reduce the terrible toll of relapse. As I see it, the only function of a Twelve Step treatment centre is to help a larger number of people to get better than would have been likely to do so through the Anonymous Fellowships alone. However, times change and just as we now have greater insight into multiple addictions than was possible sixty or more years ago at the birth of AA, so we also have to recognise that residential treatment centres are expensive and therefore unavailable to many people. Furthermore, the Twelve Step approach is not without its enemies and never more so than today. The problems of addiction in our society are increasing every day, yet Twelve Step treatment centres are being destroyed by the politics, philosophy and economics of people who oppose them even while having no understanding nor experience of them.

Such is life - but it need not be death. It is up to those of us who work in this field to find inexpensive and politically immune ways of helping addicts to recover. Relying upon charitable donations is fine for some at the expense of others: spending other people's money is a curious virtue and the resource is in any case limited. Relying upon the State is even more dangerous as policies change with governments and because the short-term economies of pharmaceutical "treatments" tend to be convincing to bureaucrats. Further, we have to accept that addicts of any kind are not generally the recipients of clinical or personal understanding. Our addictive behaviour tends not to induce sympathy in doctors, nor in the public at large. We are our own worst enemies and, as a result, we are on our own.

Yet so were the co-founders of AA - and look what they achieved with no resources and with very considerable cynical opposition. We should be so lucky to have been handed on what they gave to us!

My aims in writing are, firstly, to pay homage to Bill W. and Dr. Bob and all the others who originated and carried the message of recovery to us; secondly, to defy those who believe that destroying Twelve Step treatment centres destroys their ideas; and, thirdly, to encourage those who want happier lives, free from all addiction.

If working the Twelve Steps is hard, that's just the way it is - but it's better than the alternative.

Addicts of any kind will tend to believe that our use of mood-altering substances, behaviours or relationships is not significantly different from that of many other people. Thus, in this respect, we deny our own personal problem. The commentaries on each Step for addicts have therefore mostly been written in the first person in order to encourage individual awareness.

Compulsive helpers will tend to believe that what we do is simply a personal choice rather than an addictive behaviour that is seen in many people. Thus, in this respect, we deny our common experience with others. The commentaries on each Step for compulsive helpers have therefore been written in the plural in order to encourage corporate awareness.

Step I for Mood-altering Substances, Behaviours and Relationships.

Step I: I admit that I am powerless over the mood-altering substances, behaviours and relationships that affect me and that my life has become unmanageable.

Summary of PROMIS Core Beliefs:

1. The neurotransmission systems in the mood centres of the brain act as chemical junctions between the electrical pathways in the neurones (nerve cells). When these neurotransmission systems are defective, the basic level of mood is disturbed so that the sufferer feels constantly anxious, depressed or emotionally "empty".

2. There is increasing genetic and epidemiological evidence that neurotransmission systems are defective in some people (giving them excessive appetites for mood-altering substances, behaviours or relationships) but not in others. It follows that neurotransmission disease can neither be prevented nor treated through love, education or punishment. Genetic inheritance of a particular condition implies that the sufferer is not personally responsible for having the condition as such, although still fully responsible for all his or her behaviour towards other people. Genetic inheritance does not imply that the parents or grandparents of the sufferer necessarily had similar compulsive or addictive tendencies. They may have had other addictive outlets for neurotransmission disease or they may simply have

carried the tendency to neurotransmission disease in their genetic material without ever developing the disease itself.

3. Research at PROMIS has shown that addictive behaviours commonly come in clusters:

i   "hedonistic": the determined search for pleasure;

ii   "nurturant" (of self): soothing one's self;

iii "compulsive helping" (nurturant of others): to satisfy the need to be needed.

Both "hedonistic" and "nurturant" addictive tendencies lead the sufferer to use substances, behaviours or relationships on the basis "I need you to fix me". In compulsive helping, the addictive relationship is used on the basis "I need you to need me". As these tendencies are the mirror image of each other, it is common for compulsive helpers to marry "primary" addicts ("hedonistic" or "nurturant"). Thus, neurotransmission disease is perpetuated down the ages even though it affects only ten per cent of the population.

It is not true that all people have a tendency to be addicted to something. Addicts can be differentiated from the general population through the PROMIS questionnaires on how to identify addictive behaviour. The healthy use of mood-altering substances, behaviours or relationships is when they are used for their normal function rather than specifically for their mood-altering effect on that individual in order to quell emotional cravings.

It is also not true that addiction is caused primarily by physical, emotional or social trauma in childhood or merely through exposure to addictive substances, processes or relationships. What is probably true is that addictive or compulsive behaviour has a threefold origin:

i   Genetically inherited defect in the neurotransmission system causing a basic defect in mood;
ii   Emotional trauma that sensitises that defect and sets up a craving for mood-alteration;
iii Exposure to substances, behaviours or relationships that have a specific mood-altering effect for that individual.

Many people have experienced similar trauma or have been similarly exposed yet they develop no addiction whatever because they have no underlying genetically inherited neurotransmission disease.

Some sufferers from neurotransmission disease have one addictive cluster ("hedonistic", "nurturant" or "compulsive helping"). Some have two. Some have all three. Some people who come from addictive families have no addictive outlet whatever, although they may or may not carry the latent tendency to neurotransmission disease in their genetic material even though they do not suffer from it themselves.

4. Environmental factors may have an influence upon which particular addictive substances, processes or relationships become the chosen addictive outlets for each sufferer from neurotransmission disease.

5. Disease of the neurotransmission systems also affects the perception mechanisms of the brain so that sufferers are "in denial" : they themselves are unable to see and accept their own problem. This may in part be because they cannot conceive what life would be like without the use of mood-altering substances, behaviours and relationships.

6. Denial is countered solely through the group experience of recognising one's own behaviour in others. One-to-one therapy is counter-productive, tending to increase isolation and the belief that one is "special and different".

7. There is no intellectual impairment in sufferers from neurotransmission disease: cognitive behavioural therapy is unnecessary as well as ineffective. There is no psychiatric or psychological defect as such in sufferers from neurotransmission disease. They may coincidentally have the same psychiatric or psychological problems as anyone else, particularly those from dysfunctional families of any kind. Thus, they may receive help for their general psychiatric or psychological problems through various therapeutic approaches but none of these will be any help whatever for the underlying neurotransmission disease. Furthermore, once the sufferers are in appropriate recovery from neurotransmission disease, there will be no psychiatric or psychological problem other than those from which they may suffer coincidentally. The underlying anxiety and depression and the emotional emptiness of neurotransmission disease should resolve completely with the continuing application of the Twelve Step recovery programme.

8. Neurotransmission disease can be falsely "treated" by chemical (pharmaceutical or "recreational") substances but, unlike use of the Twelve Step recovery programme, the therapeutic dose can never be finely adjusted to suit all human circumstances on a day-to-day basis but only in "blunderbuss" fashion.

9. Neurotransmission disease is appropriately and effectively treated (and the "dose" adjusted as required on a day-to-day basis) through total abstinence from the mood-altering substances, behaviour and relationships that affect each individual and through the continuing mood-altering behaviour of reaching out to help other sufferers on an anonymous basis and working the Twelve Step programme of the Anonymous Fellowships. The mood-altering effects of the Twelve Step programme are transient and therefore have to be repeated on a regular basis. Abstinence by itself simply leads to the "dry drunk" syndrome in which the sufferer retains the mood disturbance but has no appropriate or inappropriate outlet for it.

10. Professionals working with sufferers from neurotransmission disease are not helped

themselves for their own neurotransmission disease through their professional work: they may even become self-important (and the effects of their neurotransmission disease may become worse) because their work is not done anonymously. They need the same continuing appropriate treatment for their own neurotransmission disease, through total abstinence and through working the Twelve Step programme, as do other sufferers.

11. The purpose of working the Twelve Steps is far more than merely to stop using mood-altering substances, behaviours and relationships. It is to develop an entirely new way of life, with the following characteristics:

i   full responsibility for self, not expecting other people or the state to provide;
ii   contributing to society through gainful employment or through other positive contribution;
iii mature stable relationships;
iv   peace of mind, regardless of unsolved problems;
v   creativity and enthusiasm.

12. True recovery is seen rather than heard. It shows itself in the way people live their lives, rather than in what they say.

Step I for Mood-altering Substances, Behaviours and Relationships.

Step I: I admit that I am powerless over my addiction and that my life has become unmanageable.

My life is a mess and I have lost control of some aspects of it. Some problems persist despite my repeated attempts (occasionally temporarily successful) to be in control. I have attempted to use some mood-altering substances, behaviours and relationships in order to feel better. These attempts to comfort myself have eventually turned against me: the mood-altering effects have been progressively less successful, while the damaging consequences have grown. I have felt increasing self-pity, believing that I deserve to feel better and to have a better life, and I have increasingly blamed other people, places and things for my pain. I have used some mood-altering substances, behaviours and relationships, saying that I need them, deserve them, and could not reasonably be expected to do without them.

On some occasions I have tried to give up a particular mood-altering substance, behaviour or relationship and I have felt so bad that I "had to" go back to it, thus failing to acknowledge that the bad feelings are in fact direct withdrawal effects from previous use.

On the occasions when I have succeeded in putting down one mood-altering substance, process or relationship, I have often increased my use of another. I have continued my use of mood-altering substances, processes and relationships despite the repeated serious concerns of other people and I have justified my actions (to myself if not always to them).

My way of life sometimes illustrates the very opposite of the characteristics of honesty, open-mindedness and willingness that are seen in recovery. I may have expected other people or the state to provide for me or to bail me out of my problems. I may have contributed progressively less to society. My relationships may have been immature, when I have expected other people to be sensitive to my needs and wants, irrespective of my behaviour towards them. Furthermore, my relationships have been damaged, or may even have broken down altogether, as a result of my behaviour.

Do I want to be rid of all my addictive outlets for my neurotransmission disease or do I want to hang on to some of them?

Am I frightened of change or of staying as I am?

Am I ready to take responsibility for my own life?

Step I for Compulsive Helping.

Step I: I admit that I am powerless over other people's lives and my own compulsive helping and that my life has become unmanageable.

Summary of PROMIS Core Beliefs:

1. Compulsive helping is the mirror-image of primary addiction to mood-altering substances, behaviours and relationships. Whereas the primary addict seeks something "out there" to help him or her to feel better, the compulsive helper offers himself or herself (something "in here") to other people (commonly to addicts) to help them and thereby to help himself or herself to feel needed and valued.

2. The tendency towards compulsive helping is probably also genetically inherited rather than a product of upbringing or personal behavioural choice. It is not caused by exposure to the addictive behaviour of other people.

3. Compulsive helping is not a pleasant, constructive, personality trait. It is unpleasant and destructive (however sweetly expressed and well-intentioned) because it patronises, assuming that the recipient could not manage for himself or herself, and it gets in the way of other people developing their own skills through learning from their own experience.

4. Compulsive helping is also highly destructive to the person who does it. Eternally seeking one's self-esteem from other people is exhausting and does not lead to the development of healthy relationships.

5. Compulsive helping is an addictive process, being progressive and destructive in just the

same way as any other addictive or compulsive behaviour. The "drugs" of compulsive helping are caretaking (far beyond normal caring) and self-denial (far beyond normal kindness or selflessness and into self-abasement to the level of stupidity).

6. Those of us who are both addicts and compulsive helpers will find that we tend to be the demanding and manipulating addict in some relationships and the anxious, patronising, pestering or long-suffering, compulsive helper in others. We tend to relapse into one addictive process on the pain of the other.

Step I for Compulsive Helping

Step I: I admit that I am powerless over other people's lives and my own compulsive helping and that my life has become unmanageable.

How much do I assume that I know what is best for other people? How often do I take on their pain, bailing them out for the consequences of their behaviour and preventing them from learning from their own experience? How many of my relationships have followed similar patterns? How much do I consider my own needs?

How often is it my natural instinct to keep the peace, lower the tension, quench the tears, relieve the discomfort, soften the blow, find a compromise? At first sight these look like virtues - and that is exactly what they are individually on appropriate occasions. However, when they are put all together they can be seen to be a philosophy of superiority and interference.

Supposing we always impose a compromise in quarrels between two children. The child who was wrong gets away with his or her bad behaviour, while the child who was right is not rewarded, and may in effect be punished, for good behaviour. This is exceedingly unfair. We may believe that we are giving a message of tolerance whereas in fact it is one of injustice. If this principle holds for the upbringing of children, how much more true is it for adults, especially for addicts. By failing to have the courage to take sides, have a firm view and oppose tyranny, we may indeed temporarily keep the peace - but at a terrible price.

Compulsive helping is every bit as destructive in families as any addiction can be. The parent who is enabled to continue inappropriate behaviour is just as damaging to the children whether the parent is an active addict or compulsive helper. Drunkenness, drug addiction, food obsession and the primary addictive behaviours are damaging enough in one parent without the other parent making allowances for them instead of confronting them head on. Singling out one child for special attention and favours, on some pretext of special need, can at times be fearfully damaging not only to the other children but also in particular to that selected child.

The social effects of institutionalised compulsive helping, through the activities of various professionals, from politicians and social workers to teachers and doctors, can be utterly disastrous and divisive. Compulsive helping is not a virtue: it is a well-disguised (especially from ourselves) self-aggrandising, destructive vice.

Step II for Mood-altering Substances, Behaviours and Relationships.

Step II: I have come to believe that a power greater than myself could restore me to sanity.

My determination to do things my own way is my perfect right and has resulted in many fine achievements. At times, however, it has gone too far so that I have caused myself, and sometimes other people, a lot of damage that could have been avoided if I had given up an impossible struggle earlier. I have difficulty in distinguishing between the battles which should be fought and those I should give up. Often I have fought hardest to prove that I am right over something when I am obviously wrong. Anyone could tell me I was wrong - and people often did - but I wouldn't listen.

My use of mood-altering substances, behaviours and relationships is something that I have protected to the very last, despite all the damage they have caused, because I could not see how I could do without them.

Sometimes, when I have tried to give them up, I found that I could not: I survived without them for a time - as any addict can - but felt dreadful without them and it was only a matter of time before I found a "reason" to go back to them. Then the damaging consequences of their use became even worse so that I couldn't live with the mood-altering substances, behaviours and relationships but also couldn't live without them.

Even then I was only prepared to submit (acknowledge that I had lost a particular struggle) but not to surrender (admit that I had lost the entire war). I felt that if I were to surrender I would be finished.

The great paradox of recovery, however, is when we discover that it is only when we give up trying to control our moods that we do in fact find peace of mind through learning to distinguish the things that we can change from those we cannot. This paradox has been particularly well expressed in the statement "I could not help myself until I realised that I could not help myself". In other words, self-control and the determined exercise of willpower simply do not work. Conversely, working with others in the Anonymous Fellowships, and thoroughly applying the Twelve Step programme, does work.

Far from believing that the world and other people have problems and that we have the solutions, we find that we have problems and the world and some other people have solutions.

But which other people? Previously we sought out other people who agreed with us. We closed our minds to ideas that differed from our own determined beliefs. Now we begin to realise that, if we are ever to grow, we have to begin to re-examine ideas that we thought stupid and begin to challenge those of our own ideas that we felt were most obviously correct.

Ultimately we recognised a profound truth that had eluded us (as well as confusing many people who tried to help us) for so long: irrational behaviour cannot be changed by rational methods. If we could have "pulled ourselves together", "grown-up" or "used our intelligence or willpower" we would have done so and our behaviour would have changed. But the fact is that in this particular aspect of our lives (control of our mood) we could not, irrespective of how rational the rest of our lives might be and regardless of our various achievements and distinctions.

Other people's attempts to understand and help us were insane: we knew that. But how about our own determined belief that only we could ever understand and help ourselves? This flew in the face of all the evidence. Under our own custody our lives had got worse, not better.

Cynics like us were unlikely suddenly to flip over into religious belief, without at the same time fearing that we would lose all powers of rationality. The concepts of "God" and "spirituality" seemed nothing to us if not religious. Yet what are hope, love, trust, innocence and honour if not spiritual values? They do not necessarily co-exist either with fine intellect or with religious belief, however much lip-service may be paid. These are what we had lost: we have a "spiritual" disease and these spiritual values are what we must find again. And what is God if not a concept of something greater than individual man? Clearly we also need to find a "God" or "Higher Power" (than self) of some kind.

But how? Certainly not through our own determined efforts: we know exactly where those had led us. Then we met other people who had also been in the pit of despair where we had been and who now have peace of mind, happy relationships and fulfilling, creative lives. Something had clearly worked for them (and they acknowledged that they had not achieved these things for themselves any more than we had) and we come to believe that a power greater than ourselves could restore us to sanity.

Step II for Compulsive Helping.

Step II: I have come to believe that a power greater than myself could restore me to sanity.

Initially one might assume that a compulsive helper would believe that everyone is a power greater than himself or herself. The opposite is true: compulsive helpers have an absolute conviction in the correctness of our own viewpoints and of what is right or wrong with the world and what is right or wrong for it. Granted that this is often supported by excellent personal and social values of honesty and consideration for others, nonetheless there is a level of smug superiority in "knowing" what is best for other people. Even if that "knowledge" is justified by experience in practice, however, it is still destructive: people learn best for themselves. Furthermore, it is difficult enough to "know" even a small part of one human being (it would not say much for that person if one really did "know" all of him or her), let alone "know" many others or "know" human nature. Arrogance at this level is dumbfounding.

Compulsive helpers may profess the contrary but, in effect, we believe in the correctness of our own vision: we are our own Higher Power.

Step III for Mood-altering Substances, Behaviours and Relationships.

Step III: I have made a decision to turn my will and my life over to the care of God *as I understand Him.*

Without doubt our neurotransmission disease, addictive disease, compulsive behaviour (call it what you will) "wants" us dead. The whole drive of addictive behaviour is towards self-destruction and death.

It might be helpful to imagine neurotransmission disease to be caused by a decaying process: it rots the mood centres of the brain so that spiritual values are progressively destroyed; it erodes the capacity for perception so that self-awareness progressively diminishes. It is almost as if the most treasured aspects of our lives are being eaten by a parasite.

The most fearful aspect of all this is that the progressive effects of neurotransmission disease come from within. They are not forced upon us by other people, places or things. They do not come from radiation or toxins. They are not due to dietary deficiencies or allergies. Like Alzheimer's disease, the origin is inside us; part of us. We do not become addicted as a result of injudicious experiment or wild over-indulgence. We are addicts by nature.

The emotional emptiness (regardless of our natural gifts or acquired comforts) of neurotransmission disease leads us inexorably towards substances, behaviours and relationships that make us feel better about ourselves. If the alternatives are constant depression or suicide (saying "no" to addictive substances, processes and relationships is fine in theory for those who have never experienced utter loneliness, desperate cravings or blind panic) then indeed we have taken the "sensible" option when we use those mood-altering substances, behaviours and relationships to stay alive. When that use develops problems of its own, then we are stuck and have nowhere to turn.

Yet still we turn again to mood-altering substances, behaviours and relationships in the determined quest to recapture what they once did for us. After all, nothing else ever worked for us. Our families, our homes, our work and our possessions may still all be present. (Addicts do not necessarily lose everything; nor must they do so before recognising their need for help.) But still the emptiness persists and our former "treatments" are no longer as effective as before - if at all.

So what now? When there is nowhere else to go, where do we go? The ultimate choice for us is simply "death" or "life"; nothing more complex than that. If we choose death - and many do, either physically or spiritually (with a fake life on constant medication) - then so be it and nothing more can be said. If we choose life then we have to recognise that our entire existence has to turn around and face in the opposite direction. No more self-pity: only acceptance of whatever life may bring us. No more blame or resentment: only understanding and gratitude.

If the devil is death and destruction, then God is life and creativity. Only through total abstinence, welcoming life and creativity through reaching out to help others on an anonymous basis, can we counter our neurotransmission disease each and every day by feeding it this positive mood-altering process.

Step III for Compulsive Helping.

Step III: I make a decision to turn my will and my life over to the care of God *as I understand Him.*

There are none so blind as those who will not see. There are none so unteachable as those who know all the answers already.

Compulsive helpers usually have very clear principles and a well worked-out code of morals and ethics, often based upon a specific political or religious creed. With such firm convictions (that are obviously correct) we may believe that we already have a Higher Power and therefore no need of another.

The fundamental difference between a Twelve Step programme and a specific political or religious belief is that the latter may sometimes tend to be exclusive (saying, in effect, "I am right and therefore you are wrong") whereas a Twelve Step programme is deliberately all-inclusive. In the literature of all the Anonymous Fellowships the word "God" is followed by the italicised and underlined phrase "as you understand Him". Thus, in a Twelve Step programme, a compulsive helper may keep whatever personal belief system he or she may already have but needs also at the same time to acknowledge the spiritual right of others to have a different political or religious belief or, more significantly, even none whatever.

For compulsive helpers, letting go of knowing what is right for other people is exceedingly difficult. Leaving them to get into their own difficulties, work out their own solutions and learn from them, is desperately hard for us. "Suppose he or she is damaged...", we say, "I could never forgive myself". On such an altar lives are more commonly sacrificed than saved. Addicts never learn from their behaviour while we tidy up all their messes and take their pain for them. The way further into their hell is paved with our good intentions.

Step IV for Mood-altering Substances, Behaviours and Relationships.

Step IV: I will make a searching and fearless moral inventory of myself.

Most of us look at this step in trepidation, seeing it as a fearful immoral inventory. But that isn't what it says. Our morals and ethics are the principles and values by which we live. They show themselves in our behaviour, both good and bad. Therefore if we are to examine our principles and values we have first to examine our behaviour. We have to look at this fearlessly (accurately) if we are to understand ourselves.

We sometimes like to believe that we do things because of our environment or because of what other people do to us. We answer the telephone because it rings. We are unpleasant to someone because he or she was unpleasant to us. But we do in fact have a choice: we don't have to answer the telephone and we ourselves do not have to behave unpleasantly, whatever other people's behaviour may be to us. In each and every case we act on our own belief system, often simply out of habit, because we never stop to think about it. We may never have asked ourselves whether we do in fact have to follow a particular course of action simply because we have always done so.

The fourth step inventory gives me an opportunity not only to look at the circumstances and events of my life, and look at my actions and reactions, but also the opportunity to see patterns in my thought processes and behaviour.

Writing a lengthy narrative is probably not very constructive (and it may be no more than a self-indulgent autobiography) because it does not put down the material in a form that can easily be examined for patterns of behaviour and underlying principles and values.

Nevertheless, each of us does our own inventory in whatever way feels most natural and appropriate for us. The important thing is to be honest and thorough rather than merely exhaustive, covering page after page of detail that actually obscures the true pattern of our behaviour.

One way of doing an inventory is simply to make lists of circumstances and events and our actions and reactions in the various major stages of our lives and in our current significant relationships. I should at the end be able to see the over-all shape of my life and be prepared to acknowledge that I myself largely shaped it that way (other than in my early childhood), irrespective of events over which I had no control and irrespective of what other people did to me. By acknowledging my own capacity to influence my own reactions to events and to other people, I begin to take responsibility for the one person I can change (through working the Twelve Step programme): myself.

Step IV for Compulsive Helping.

Step IV: I will make a searching and fearless moral inventory of myself.

Initially Step IV holds no fears whatever for a compulsive helper. We take our own inventory all day every day. We are for ever wondering what we might have done wrong or could do better for other people. But in that very process lies the destructive power of our own addictive disease: through our compulsive helping we do not help others (in spiritual terms, irrespective of what we may do for them practically) and we do considerable damage to our own lives both practically and spiritually.

Self-sacrifice is a desecration of our God-given lives, whatever our concept of God. To do something for someone else is nice and kind and helps to create a caring society - but only under two conditions:

i.   that what we do does not damage someone else's capacity for growth;
ii.   that we do not damage or destroy the gift of our own lives in the process.

By saying "Oh, I don't matter", we sow the seeds of a vile creed: that individuals should not live for their own happiness (because happiness can only be at the expense or disregard of others) and that true happiness therefore comes from self-abasement. On such a wretched philosophy the inquisitions and mass murders of religious or political tyrants are based. Self-image determines actions towards other people.

Respect for all life, starting with our own, is the central spiritual message of the Twelve Steps.

Step V for mood-altering substances, behaviours and relationships.

Step V: I admit to God, to myself and to another human being the exact nature of my wrongs.

There is a lot more to Step V than simply reading out the negative parts of Step IV. All the steps are studies in honesty and humility but Step V is the first time that someone else is involved in the process.

To myself I have admitted many things many times, sometimes casually - almost jokingly - and sometimes seriously, but most commonly in maudlin self-pity. To other people I usually bluff and posture, making out that I know more, do more and am more than is the truth. To God ... well, that's another story ... perhaps at the day of judgement ...

The day of judgement is here now - and also the day of atonement. Step V, if I do it thoroughly and really mean it, gives me the opportunity to experience both the judgement and the personal penalty at the same time and then begin a new life.

The whole point of admitting something to God is that, whatever my concept of God, there is nothing to be gained by lying or by telling half-truths. If I am to get the full value of Step V, I can do so only by digging down past my pretences and justifications. This is not the time for explanations and rationalisations: those times are past.

The other person is necessary, partly to ensure that I do not duck the issue and produce yet another of my great performances that say everything and mean nothing, and partly to enable the process to be a rite of passage: I go through it at a specific time and I come out different.

The process of Step V enables me to get rid of the ghosts that haunt me. When I face up to them totally honestly, and accept my responsibility for them, they lose their power. They damaged my past but no longer will they be able to damage my present and future. I clear them out of my head, leaving only the acknowledgement that, in Steps VIII and IX, I have to make total amends to those I have harmed. The more seriously I take Step V, and the more I accept my responsibility for my behaviour towards other people, then the more clear I shall be of crippling shame at the end of it. My life will be mine again.

One simple technique that may help me to gain maximum benefit is to make a short summary of the "worst" things I have done: the things I could never tell anybody - and tell these things first. When the worst is out, the immense sense of relief enables me to relax, slow down, go into more detail and get rid of it all, once and for all.

Step V for Compulsive Helping.

Step V: I admit to God, to myself and to another human being the exact nature of my wrongs.

We compulsive helpers are delighted to admit our wrongs. When the addict acknowledges that he or she has stolen something or injured somebody, we promptly chime in that we too are criminals, as testified by a solitary parking ticket (brought about when waiting to help someone else). Furthermore, we may fail to understand the difference between compulsion and habit or temptation. In trying to empathise or sympathise with the addict, or encourage him or her, we do in fact patronise. Then, in self-immolation, we scan the seven deadly sins, or other behavioural check-lists, in order to work out how we can put ourselves into the worst categories.

That process itself is our own wrong: unintentionally (but factually nonetheless) we belittle other peoples' acknowledgement of their wrongs. By care-taking for them - trying to diminish their pain of self-assessment - we get in the way of their spiritual recovery. Also, through self-denial - taking other peoples' pain on to ourselves - we damage our own lives. Yet what is more God-given - and therefore more to be treasured and nurtured - than our own lives?

At core is our misunderstanding of the word "selfish". We believe that caring for ourselves, expressing our own needs, is a vice perpetrated at other people's expense. Nothing could be further from the truth: it is in our self-interest to be kind and considerate to other people and also to ourselves. By treating ourselves differently from other people (rather than as other people) we set ourselves apart from them, above them. Such arrogance is unattractive.

Step VI for mood-altering substances, behaviours and relationships.

Step VI: I will become entirely ready to have God remove all my defects of character.

Steps VI and VII are the central spiritual steps of the Twelve Step programme. They are commonly called "the forgotten steps" because they are often overlooked in the rush towards Steps VIII and IX so that we can make amends, salve our guilty consciences, and hopefully get some amends in return. But they are forgotten at our peril: if a Twelve Step programme is not fundamentally spiritual it is nothing.

Our defects of character should by now be obvious. The advantage of doing Step IV thoroughly and methodically is that our defects of character (the misguided principles and values upon which our behaviour was based) now stare us in the face.

Wanting them to be removed is not as obvious as might at first appear. Some of them are so familiar through regular practice that we wonder who and what we would be without them. Others are not so easy to give up because we may be reluctant to do so: we feel justified in our resentments and exasperated by any suggestion that we should change while others do not (or at least we resent making our changes before they make theirs). Further, we may quite simply not want to change: this is the way we are and other people can take us or leave us.

A complicating factor is that our family and friends may even implore us not to change too much. They explain this to us on the basis of reassurance that we are not all bad (we may never have thought we were!) but the truth may be more sinister: they may like to keep us in the role of "problem" and they may even be concerned that they themselves might be next in line for self-examination.

At any stage in the Twelve Step programme - or in life - we can opt to make no further changes. But we shall pay the consequences of that stagnation. We grow or we shrivel; we change for the better or we regress. The world does not stay still, nor do relationships, and we cannot afford simply to stay static. As with all living things, we change or die, in this case spiritually and therefore ultimately physically.

Our spirits reflects our whole life and every aspect of our life, physical, mental, emotional and practical, and our spiritual life is expressed in our behaviour towards ourselves and others. Defects in our character damage everything and taint every relationship. Is that really what we want to perpetuate?

I might then say that, surely, all I have to do is to make up my mind to change, and do so. Certainly there is an element of truth in that because no change will ever take place unless I make up my mind to change and then take specific appropriate action to do so. But I have made up my mind and tried to change my compulsive or addictive behaviour many times before - and failed many times before. That means that I have failed so far to discover the specific appropriate action that works in the long term.

Asking for help is never easy. Recognising the need for help seems humiliating. But it is not: it is simply an act of acceptance and humility and there is all the difference in the world between humiliation (being humbled by someone else) and humility (accepting that I myself am not omnipotent, infallible and impregnable - in short, not God).

Asking help from God requires the belief in some form of God who would listen, who would care, and who would have the power to act. Some people find this God in various religious beliefs. Others most definitely do not. The beauty and miracle of the Twelve Step programme is that it accommodates both. "God, as you understand Him" is all that is required of belief in order to make the necessary acknowledgement "I am not God: I do not have all the answers myself: I cannot survive in isolation".

In the Anonymous Fellowships, in the very essence of their anonymity, there are people who will listen, who care (if only because their own continuing recovery depends upon reaching out to help others, thus "keeping what we give away") and who have the insight and power to help us through example.

If I want lasting recovery I have to take the specific appropriate action that works: reaching out to help others on an anonymous basis and with no thought whatever of gain for myself, other than the maintenance of my own continuing recovery.

If I want my inter-relationship with other people to be my God, the relationship has to be mutual. If I want a sense of love or hope or peace of mind then I have to go to any lengths to provide these for others, taking my mind off myself (and all my woes and resentments) and concentrating totally on them. My action in reaching out to help others on an anonymous basis is God-like in itself and this helps me, provided that I am absolutely genuine in seeking help for the other person rather than acting out of smug self-satisfaction. By being selfless I discover myself and I am then able to attain my full potential in every aspect of my life.

The prize is there for the taking - but am I ready to take the specific appropriate action that leads towards it or do I want to go on doing it my way?

Step VI for Compulsive Helping.

Step VI: I have become entirely ready to have God remove all my defects of character.

Again, we compulsive helpers are almost eager to look at our anger, greed, deceit, depravity and all the other defects of character that we find on addicts' check-lists. The very fact that we look at their literature at all, very often before they look at it themselves (well, we were only trying to be helpful, weren't we?), is indicative of our own specific defects as compulsive helpers: caretaking and self-denial.

Are we ready to give up these defects? Can we live without them or will life lose its point? Just supposing someone did get damaged, could we ever live with ourselves and with the belief that we might just possibly have done something to prevent that damage? Because of that fear (compulsion) are we never going to acknowledge how much damage our compulsive helping has done in real life, both to others and to ourselves?

Yes indeed, we may at times have been angry, greedy, deceitful, depraved and all the rest and we can certainly look at that. But, as with anyone who looks at the motes in other peoples' eyes rather than the beam in his or her own, when are we going to look at the real issue: helping is a virtue; compulsive helping - with its caretaking and self-denial - is a vice or, at any rate, an illness.

Step VII for mood-altering substances, behaviours and relationships.

Step VII: I humbly ask Him to remove my shortcomings.

Looking at my list of shortcomings (simply another name for defects of character), I can see that I do not need or want them any more. But supposing I swing across to the opposite extreme. Is being creepy and wet any better than being arrogant and hostile? Humility is putting myself alongside other people, neither above nor below them. It is the process of rejoining the human race.

Step VII is first and foremost about balance. We all know people who have become single-issue fanatics. They are particularly unattractive companions because of their tense absolutism. Whatever the topic of interest or conversation they somehow bring it round to their own preoccupation. We know that discussion is pointless and argument unproductive. Is that what we want for ourselves - a closed mind and proselytising zeal? Surely not.

The Anonymous Fellowship "slogans", such as "Live and let live" and "Easy does it", remind us to be tolerant of those who may disagree with us. After all, we are more likely to learn from those who have a different perspective than from those who only see things the way we do.

The Twelve Steps are practical rather than metaphysical and none more so than Step VII. If we come face to face with God only at the end of our lives, we might reckon on getting away with all sorts of things provided we say sorry at the last minute. However, if our God is present in the here and now, such as in our relationships with other people, then we are conscious of our behaviour all the time. With such a concept of God (the love and enthusiasm we find in our relationships with other people), our shortcomings have obvious practical damaging consequences.

Focusing on getting the best out of ourselves and other people in our relationships with them gives us a highly practical daily contact with the God of our understanding and a daily opportunity to be rid of our shortcomings. The quest for creativity in ourselves and in our relationships with other people reminds us that the derivation of the word enthusiasm comes from the Greek words *en theos* (God within).

Step VII for Compulsive Helping.

Step VII: I humbly ask Him to remove my shortcomings.

Yet again, we compulsive helpers are prepared to go through the routine. Of course we are: we've done it all our lives. We've apologised, wondered how we could be so thoughtless and stupid, prayed for forgiveness, and so on and so on, until by all accounts we should be whiter than white - and then some. Yet still the inner shame clings to us, however many times we acknowledge guilt for our actions.

And yet again we are on the wrong track. It is our preparedness for self-immolation, always putting ourselves at the bottom of the pile instead of in whatever may be our appropriate or rightful place, that causes other people and ourselves so much damage. If we have natural gifts of intelligence, musicianship, or hand/eye co-ordination, do we believe it is truly helpful to anyone for us to deny these talents or make out that everyone has equivalent attributes of some kind?

It is simply not true that everyone has talents of equal value, although differing in kind. If we have special abilities then by all means let us use them to benefit others - but we can only do so if we acknowledge and exploit, rather than deny, them. Equally, we can only be truly helpful to others if we acknowledge their limitations, neither critically nor pityingly but with acceptance of reality.

Interfering in other people's lives because we have a great vision for them spells exploitation and, yet again, arrogance.

Step VIII for mood-altering substances, behaviours and relationships.

Step VIII: I will make a list of all persons I have harmed and become willing to make amends to them all.

Addicts rather enjoy this Step because we know that at some time in our list we can write the word "MYSELF". Oh the melodrama! Oh the self-pity! Oh yes, oh yes, let's wallow in it!

The truth is that we certainly have damaged ourselves every time we hurt someone else, because we ourselves are a part of each and every one of our relationships. The way to make amends to ourselves is therefore to make amends to the other people we have harmed. When I have completed my amends to them there will be no need of further amends to myself.

As any addict worthy of the name will know, we are all capable of flying from one extreme to the other. In Step VIII we believe either that we have never harmed anybody at all (well, not intentionally anyway ... and, well, they did in some ways contribute to it themselves ... and, come to think of it, they caused us a fair degree of harm: so what about that then?) or that we have harmed everyone we ever met (which is manifestly untrue and simply another defence, protecting us from facing up to the full reality of the harm we have done to some particular people, especially to those closest to us).

If we go back to our Step IV inventory and to the Step VI list of our defects of character, we can work out who we have harmed at each stage of our lives and as a result of each of our defects of character. We shall probably discover that it is largely the same people who get harmed time and time again. The sadness of that realisation (that we hurt most the people we love most) is one of the most difficult moments of the entire recovery programme.

Nonetheless there are other people, who are not as close to us, and sometimes even total strangers, whom we have harmed by our compulsive or addictive behaviour, or through the preoccupations and self-obsession brought about by our defects of character. Those people need to be on the list even if we do not know their names. The process of recovery involved in Step VIII depends not so much on the practical possibilities of making amends (that is the subject of Step IX) but on our genuine and absolute willingness to do so.

Step VIII for Compulsive Helping.

Step VIII: I will make a list of all the persons I have harmed, and become willing to make amends to them all.

Learning to respond only when asked for help, and to offer only the facts of our experience rather than well-meaning advice, does not come naturally to compulsive helpers. Indeed we do rush in where angels fear to tread.

The angels are right to fear treading on other people's lives. With new insight into compulsive helping as a progressive and destructive addictive disease, we can look back and see just how much damage this process has done to the lives of others and to ourselves.

As compulsive helpers, the harm we have done to others is through doing too much:

i.   We have given them too much so that they became dependent rather than developing their own capacity for independence;
ii. We have bailed them out of their difficulties, buying into their own sob-stories or into the threats of others.

The harm we have done to ourselves is through doing too little:

i.   What time, money, energy and enthusiasm do we have left for our own pleasure and personal development in the simple joys of living?

ii. How much do we truly value our own lives, other than in some macabre concept of serving others to the extent of our own self-destruction and death?

Step IX for mood-altering substances,behaviours and relationships

Step IX: I will make direct amends to such people wherever possible, except when to do so would injure them or others.

There are clear stages in making amends. I need to follow them carefully and sensitively.

i. Working out in advance precisely what I have done and what it is appropriate to say, bearing in mind the need to avoid making matters worse for the other person.
ii. Contacting the other person and finding a time convenient for him or her. (If the person is difficult to find, imagine that he or she owes me a large sum of money!)
iii. Getting straight to the point and saying what it is that I have done. (There is no need for any flowery explanation of why I am doing this: a simple explanation that I have something on my conscience will suffice.)
iv. Saying sorry.
v. Asking what amends the other person would like. (At this point it is appropriate to say that it matters to me that amends should be made. Money should be paid for things I have taken, even if the other person is rich enough for that sum to be trivial. If I have no money then I can offer a skill that I do possess or I can offer time - a commodity that busy people might readily appreciate.)
vi. If the other person really does not want amends (and I should neither hope for this nor look for it) then accept his or her kindness simply and gratefully. If he or she reacts negatively to the information I have given him or her, that is his or her absolute right and I have to accept it as a consequence of my own previous damaging behaviour, rather than see it as a defect in that person.
vii. Do not do whatever it was again. (This is perhaps the most important amends that we can make to the people who are close to us.)

When the person to whom I wish to make amends is unknown I can do something anonymously for someone else.

When the person is dead or untraceable I can give something to, or do something for, another person or for a cause I believe that person would value.

The Twelve Promises (from page 83 of the "Big Book" of Alcoholics Anonymous) are often read out at meetings of the Anonymous Fellowships without any acknowledgement that they refer specifically to working Step IX: "If we are painstaking about this phase of our development ...". I need to acknowledge that if I am to progress.

Step IX for Compulsive Helping.

Step IX: I will make direct amends to such people wherever possible, except when to do so would injure them or others.

For compulsive helpers, making amends is certainly tricky and requires some thought. How does one say "I'm sorry I helped you"?

In fact that is not the issue at all and looking at it that way simply perpetuates the myth that compulsive helping is a nice process that has gone too far. This is exactly the same as believing that alcoholism comes from drinking too much, that drug addiction comes from unwise experiment, and that eating disorders are the consequence of childhood abuse, of reading fashion magazines, or of following the wrong diet. Compulsive helping is as different from normal helping as alcoholism is from normal drinking (which is when one likes the taste rather than because one wants to change the way one feels about oneself) or as different as any other addictive process is from the counterpart enjoyed by non-addictive people.

Thus we can readily say "I think I patronised you and damaged you by doing too much, by interfering in your life, and by not trusting your capacity to find your own way through life's difficulties and I'm sorry for that".

We may or may not be understood - particularly not if the person whom we have harmed is an addict who is still using mood-altering substances, behaviours or relationships and still relying upon us to pick up the pieces. Under such circumstances we may get a barrow-load of abuse along with spine-chilling stories of what will happen to the poor, defenceless, incapable addict if we withdraw our support. Too bad. Even so, we do need to be sensitive in making our amends with love and understanding, rather than doing so as yet another act of proving that we know what is good for other people better than they know for themselves.

Making amends to ourselves starts first and foremost with the belief that we are worth it and with the acknowledgement that compulsive helping really has damaged our lives and that it is not a virtue that we have simply overdone. If we haven't grasped that (and it really is difficult to do so, not least because we really haven't done anything significantly wrong - in the legal sense - in this aspect of our lives) then we need to go back through the Steps all over again.

Step X for mood-altering substances, behaviours and relationships.

Step X: I will continue to take a personal inventory and when I am wrong promptly admit it.

Steps X, XI and XII are the "maintenance Steps" that we do every day in order to prevent relapse. We sometimes hear people emphasising that they do Steps I, II and III every day, focusing on their powerlessness. Surely this should have been accepted long ago. The whole purpose of working through the Steps is so that we can move on and take full responsibility for our lives. Far from continuing to be powerless (except over the use of mood-altering substances, behaviours or relationships) we gain the power (or, to be precise, we are given it: the paradox of recovery is that it is a gift that we did not deserve and that we often did everything we possibly could to reject) to manage our lives appropriately alongside other people.

Just as people who wear spectacles can thereby overcome their short sight (and do not self-consciously show off the fact that they are doing so), people who work a Twelve Step programme as a matter of absolute course in their lives can trust in its effectiveness. To discard the Twelve Step programme after a time would be just as crazy and dangerous as discarding spectacles in the belief that one no longer needs them after using them for a long time.

The first part of Step X is easy: provided that I remember to do it as part of automatic daily discipline even when I am tired and fed up (or, for that matter, happy and exhilarated).

The second part is difficult. Admitting that I am wrong at the very time that I am wrong is fiendishly hard - until I discover how much other people appreciate it. The problem then is that my addictive nature will look for further opportunities to be whiter than white or holier than thou. Hence the need for daily vigilance. However long it may be since my last use of mood-altering substances, behaviours or relationships, my addictive nature does not go away. I may no longer have daily problems with the use of mood-altering substances, behaviours or relationships (although it should always be remembered that it says in the "Big Book" of Alcoholics Anonymous - hopefully not as an invitation to relapse - that "no one among us is capable of perfect adherence to this programme") but I still have a problem with me.

Step X for Compulsive Helping.

Step X: I will continue to take personal inventory and when I am wrong promptly admit it.

It is said that when compulsive helpers are drowning, someone else's life passes before our eyes. By the time we reach Step X we should have a better appreciation of the value of our own lives.

Those of us who are both addicts and compulsive helpers may believe, on reflecting over the course of our lives, that our primary addiction caused a great deal of damage to other people whereas our compulsive helping caused a great deal of damage to ourselves. In truth however, the more we take our own inventory, the more we discover that both primary addiction and compulsive helping damage both ourselves and other people equally.

The purpose of recovery from any addictive process is to regain a normal life. Addicts will never be able to recapture the ability to use mood-altering substances (such as alcohol, drugs, nicotine and sugar and refined carbohydrates) sensibly because we never had that capacity in the first place: we were born with our addictive tendency. Addictive behaviours or relationships, however, are slightly different in so far as we have to retain the behaviour (exercising, risk-taking, shopping or spending, working etc) but learn to use it for its primary purpose rather than for mood-altering effect.

Correspondingly, compulsive helpers have to learn how to help normally and avoid being compulsive helpers. This process is easier than it first appears. All we have to do is to ask ourselves (and confirm in our daily inventory) if the purpose of a particular course of action is to be genuinely helpful, and in response to a request, or whether our aim is to satisfy our addictive need to be needed.

And when we do make an error and compulsively help, rather than respond appropriately to a request for help, do we now have the insight (and the guts) to see what we have done and promptly admit it, rather than find a worthy reason that explains or justifies it to others and to ourselves?

Step XI for mood-altering substances, behaviour and relationships.

Step XI: I will seek through prayer and meditation to improve my conscious contact with God as I understand Him, praying only for knowledge of His will for me and the power to carry that out.

Anyone who has ever said "God help me" or "Good God!" or even "For God's sake" has, perhaps unwittingly, said a prayer. An acknowledgement of inability to control events, a statement of wonder, or even an imploring for something to happen or not, are all recognitions of something greater than self.

Anyone who has marvelled at a sunset, been mesmerised by a candle flame, or relaxed in a warm bath while listening to gentle music, has meditated. Taking a brief respite from the hurly-burly of the day and pondering the infinite is meditation enough without the need for mystical performance and funny smells.

Prayer and meditation, perfectly straightforward, normal, healthy activities, have been high-jacked by professionals and made to appear as if the rest of us can appreciate their beauty and wonder only on special licence. We need to reclaim them for ourselves.

Some prayers may have universal appeal, such as the prayer attributed to St Francis of Assisi, the "Serenity" Prayer (the first part of a much longer prayer by Reinhold Niebuhr), and also the Step III Prayer from the "Big Book" of Alcoholics Anonymous:

"God, I offer myself to Thee - to build with me and to do with me as Thou wilt.

Relieve me of the bondage of self, that I may better do Thy will. Take away my difficulties, that victory over them may bear witness to those I would help of Thy Power, Thy Love, and Thy Way of life. May I do Thy will always!"

Each one of us may have favourite prayers, gleaned from religious texts of various beliefs. They may say something special to us or they may be comforting through familiarity. A poem or some other piece of literature may also be a prayer, in its expression of beauty and awe, despite being secular. A simple wish or a statement of gratitude can be a prayer (known as an "arrow" prayer because of its directness) and it is certainly no less of a prayer for being short, simple and straightforward.

Recitation has value if it acts as a constant reminder. It has perhaps less value if it is merely repeated without thought. Contemplation is an activity of a restful mind, but it is no less an activity for being restful. By contrast, the triviality of the quick fix is as much a cause for despair as are its short-lived effects.

In reflecting upon the great mysteries of life (such as the three fundamental questions "Where did I come from?", "What am I doing?" and "Where am I going?") we can, if we so wish, turn to religious and mystical writings and practices if we find practical help in doing so.

Alternatively, we can write our own prayers and meditations, seeking our own personal spiritual goal.

For each of us our concept of God will work for us when we feel that it is conscious and specifically relevant in our lives. Spiritual growth may be attainable through religious belief but the world's wars are often fought on sectarian divisions, and a modern scientific education does not look kindly upon mysticism, so some of us may choose to formulate our own spiritual path. If we do so, however, we need to be aware of the risk of returning to the arrogant belief of all using addicts: that we are right and everyone else is wrong. Seeking to separate ourselves from the rest of humanity is what we did before - and look where that got us.

Acceptance, tolerance, forgiveness, love, tenderness, gentleness, hope, trust, honour, innocence, happiness, peace of mind, confidence, ease and grace: these spiritual values are surely God's will for us - whatever our concept of God. Doing everything I can to bring these values into my own life is a worthy recognition of the gift of life itself.

My own daily prayers and my own daily meditations - seeking deeper values in my life than my professional and personal preoccupations - bring me closer to conscious contact with the God of my own understanding.

Do I have the power to achieve clarity of value and purpose in my life? Yes indeed I do - if I get out of my own way.

Step XI for Compulsive Helping.

Step XI: I will seek through prayer and meditation to improve my conscious contact with God as I understand Him, praying only for knowledge of His will for me and the power to carry that out.

So what is God's will for compulsive helpers? We always imagined that it was to serve others and to help to make the world a better place. And so it may well be - but it is certainly not to be compulsive helpers, getting in everyone else's way with our self-righteous absolute knowledge of what is right for them and our determination to see our chosen path to glory through to the end, however much we ourselves may suffer in the process.

Control is the name of the game. Are we still determined to be in control or can we yet trust the God of our understanding to run the show? As compulsive helpers, can we get on with the straightforward practical business of running our own lives and leave others to run their own lives, make their own mistakes and learn from them?

Do we have the power to "Live and let live" and to "Let go and let God"? If not we had better pray for it (try it out in our relationships with others and ask other recovering compulsive helpers for their insight if we get into difficulty) and meditate upon it (take some quiet time for ourselves to ponder the spiritual abyss into which our addictive compulsive helping has led us).

When we have done that, might we allow ourselves to pray and meditate on the concept of happiness? Ultimately God's will for us (whatever our understanding of God) must be for us to live normal, healthy and happy lives. With our compulsive helping in recovery on a day-to-day basis, we can do so.

Step XII for mood-altering substances, behaviours and relationships.

Step XII: Having had a spiritual awakening as the result of these Steps, I try to carry this message to others who still suffer and to practise these principles in all my affairs.

Those of us who have worked for a university degree and have also worked a Twelve Step programme will often readily acknowledge that the degree was the easier task. This is because the Twelve Step programme is not an intellectual exercise but a spiritual path. (There may be a few people who are too intellectually impaired to be able to work a Twelve Step programme but there are a considerable number who may be too clever by half.) To be sure, we have to think about it but, most of all, we have to do it: it is entirely based upon action. Running a marathon is easy by comparison: you train for it, run it in an afternoon and it's all over. Working a Twelve Step programme takes a lifetime, one day at a time.

When we first come to meetings of the Anonymous Fellowships we may happily imagine that all we have to do is to sit back and let recovery come to us. Other people reach out to help us unstintingly, giving us the benefit of their experience, strength and hope. It takes time for us to realise that that is the way that they get better and that we shall have to follow their exact example if we are to get and keep recovery of our own.

The gradual and inexorable process of taking our minds off ourselves and on to other people is grindingly hard in working through the Twelve Steps and it is not over when it's over: it starts again each day. Granted it gets progressively easier as time goes on, but if we ever become complacent we relapse. It's as simple as that, although not necessarily as immediate. It often takes quite some time to throw away our physical abstinence even though our value system and our behaviour towards other people may decline very quickly.

A spiritual awakening may be a sudden process like a flash of light in the sky (although this is perhaps more commonly the result of a stellar supernova or the intra-cerebral perception of light caused by a detached retina) but it is usually experienced gradually and retrospectively. It is only when we look back over the mountain ranges that we have climbed that we realise that we have reached some sort of a summit - or at least we can see that we are higher up than we were before.

The development of Twelve Step residential treatment centres has been a mixed blessing. They have the capacity to help people through the difficult initial days or weeks of timid recovery and thus they should at least double the number of men and women who would have got better through working the Twelve Step programme simply in the Anonymous Fellowships and without further therapeutic aid. However, treatment centres may have the disadvantage of putting an unjustified emphasis on professional therapy of one kind or another, rather than reinforcing our continuing dependence upon working the Twelve Steps. The "Big Book" of Alcoholics Anonymous is absolutely and specifically clear on this point: "These are the Steps we took..."
Most dangerous of all is the effect that providing therapy for others can have on counselling staff who are themselves in recovery. Failure to remember where we ourselves came from, and failure to work our own Twelve Step programme anonymously alongside other addicts (irrespective of whatever we may have been doing all day in our professional work), spells arrogance, dishonesty, resentment and disaster.

Carrying the message to others does not imply success. Very often we do not succeed in the aim of helping the other person. Yet still we succeed in our aim of perpetuating our own recovery by keeping what we attempted to give away. This same principle (keeping what we give away) is what we try to show to others but we have to remember that, although we may love them, we cannot do their loving for them: we can set an example of love and provide a loving environment but we can only do our own loving.

The Twelve Step programme is practical to the very last. What use would it all be if not in order to apply the principles of honesty, open-mindedness and willingness (the H-O-W of recovery) in all our affairs? To have one set of principles for Anonymous Fellowship meetings and another for home and the office would be both daft and impossible. The great truth and the great gift of the Twelve Step programme is that it is a programme for life.

Step XII for Compulsive Helping.

Step XII: Having had a spiritual awakening as the result of these Steps, I try to carry this message to compulsive helpers who still suffer, and to practise these principles in all my affairs.

Spiritual awakening after a lifetime of addiction of any kind is glorious. For compulsive helpers the relief of no longer having to run everyone else's lives as well as our own is especially glorious. We have got our own lives back from the clutches of our addiction!

What shall we now do with our lives? The great risk for compulsive helpers is that we promptly ask ourselves how we can be truly helpful to others - and off we go into the pit again. But in fact we can be helpful to others, as specifically required in this Step. The beneficiaries of our help, however, should be other compulsive helpers who still suffer.

Our whole tendency on learning about the processes of addictive disease and recovery will be to want to become professional counsellors so that we can be helpful to addicts. The risks of that process should be obvious but, as compulsive helpers, we tend to be oblivious to risks of that nature: our cause of helping others is good and great and any risk is worthwhile!

Conversely, our attitude towards other compulsive helpers tends to be that they are a bit pathetic. We may even believe that they have not yet found out how to be really helpful, as we were and can certainly now be. Back comes the arrogance; off goes the disease again.

But it need not be like that if we remember our own journey through the Steps and focus on reaching out to help other compulsive helpers on an anonymous basis, remembering one golden rule and spiritual principle in all our affairs: leave other people (especially addicts) alone to get on with their own lives, while we get on with our own.

Humility

1. Arrogance, the belief that we are special and different, is the central character defect brought about by addictive disease. Disregarding the feelings and needs of others, we become engrossed in blame and self-pity.

2. Humility, recognising our fellowship with others and the need for a Higher Power than self, is the basis of the entire Twelve Step programme.

Step I shows us that, left to ourselves, our lives have become chaotic, a product of self-will run riot.

Step II acknowledges that, however determinedly we tried to control our thoughts, feelings and behaviour, we have in fact lost control and need a Higher Power than self to get it back.

Step III recognises the need to get out of the driving seat of our spiritual lives and hand over to a more competent force that can guide us towards hope, trust, honour, love, innocence and other spiritual values, thus putting our lives back on course towards having some relevance.

Step IV forces us to see through our own denial.

Step V examines every last crevice that helped us to hide from the truth of our condition.

Step VI gets us ready to welcome defeat.

Step VII bows us down, challenging each last pathetic, arrogant, resistance.

Step VIII lists those we have harmed, irrespective of what they have done to us.

Step IX demands our amends to them, considering their perspectives rather than our own.

Step X keeps us focused on our own behaviour, challenging our self-justifications.

Step XI maintains our new-found sense of ultimate individual insignificance, and directs our constructive daily efforts away from self-centredness, channelling them towards wider spiritual awareness.

Step XII rejoices in what we have been given undeservedly and reminds us that we can keep it only by giving it away to others, by replacing self-seeking with generosity, and ensuring that we keep ourselves free from our previous stagnation, deceit and self-importance.

Learning

1. There are none so unteachable as those who already know all the answers.

2. The blind are the best people to teach the newly blind: they understand the difficulties and the perspectives and they don't patronise.

3. Learning something new may involve far more than building on what we already know: our existing knowledge may in fact get in the way and we may have to discard it in order to look at a problem in an entirely new way in order to find a new solution.

4. The most valuable teachers may be those who have only recently learnt: they may still understand the insecurity and bewilderment of ignorance and not yet be carried away by their own knowledge and importance.

5. We learn most from those who are working alongside us on the same problems.

6. If we want to learn about an illness we should go to where it is endemic or even epidemic. E.g., addicts learn best from recovering addicts.

7. The most perceptive teachers are those whose lives depended upon what they learnt and now teach.

8. A successful teacher is more interested in the pupils than in himself or herself.

9. The best way to clarify our thinking on a subject is to teach an audience that will challenge our concepts and methods.

10. We can't listen when we are planning what we ourselves are going to say. We can't hear when we are talking.

11. The memory and perception mechanisms of the brain do not work well, if at all, when it is drugged in any way or when it is preoccupied.

12. If we do not learn and re-learn through constant repetition, we forget.

13. The most useful, but also potentially the most damaging, aspect of the human mind is its capacity for selective forgetting.

14. The desire to learn is far more than a wish to avoid further pain and it is not achieved simply by making a one-off decision: it is a continuing personal philosophy.

15. Knowledge and understanding are not at all the same thing.

16. Even when we believe we know all that is currently known in a subject, there is still more to learn.

An Attitude of Gratitude

1. It has been said that religion is for those who are frightened of going to hell whereas spirituality is for those of us who have been there.

2. To have been helped, when we had done everything in our power not to deserve it, is awesome.

3. Addicts are the fun people. We were adventurous from the very beginning, always seeking to make sense of a crazy world, learning to take risks and suffer the consequences when things go wrong, picking ourselves up and starting again when we got battered. We give life our best shot. But our addictive disease knows all this and turns our energy and enthusiasm to its own advantage. We provide the fuel for our own destruction.

4. Yet, in the blackness of utter despair, other addicts (of all people) reached out to help us. We had sought help from all sorts of professional people, as well as from friends and family, but had simply become confused by contradictory advice, and dispirited by their well-meaning attempts to understand a problem they could never understand. Into this pit strolls a "recovering" addict or two, acknowledging that they have been where we have been and showing us quite clearly that their lives are very different now. They appealed not to our sense of self-pity and blame, as so many therapists had done, but to our curiosity.

5. We identified with them and then, through the Anonymous Fellowships, with others like them. Gradually the layers of defiance, bitterness, resentment, guilt and shame are peeled away. We come to see that we ourselves created our own problems and we accept our responsibility for our damaged relationships. We acknowledge that we are addicts by nature but nonetheless accept our responsibility for our damaged relationships and for our behaviour as it affects other people.

6. As the years go by we see other addicts come and go. Some stay in recovery, some relapse. Some live happy, productive lives. Some die in the full throes of active addiction. We marvel that we ourselves survive. It seems to depend so much upon chance. Yet all we do to remain in recovery is to work the Twelve Step programme of the Anonymous Fellowships on a day-to-day basis and reach out to help other addicts. The recovery programme is so simple - but why did we take so long in coming to accept it and why do so many others reject it or fail to work it successfully? What had we done to deserve such riches as contentment in our daily lives, peace of mind in spite of unsolved problems, mutually fulfilling relationships, and simple fun and unselfconscious laughter, such as we had never known before? The short answer is … nothing: all this is a gift. All we had to do was to get out of our own way.

7. It's a wonderful world and life is lovely. It all depends on how we view it: with the diseased eye of cynicism and suspicion or with gratitude.

Faith

1. Some words conjure up images of particular professions or practices:

    i.   health signifies the medical profession - except that they know more about disease;
    ii.   learning signifies teachers - although they may teach by rote and lack understanding;
    iii. caring signifies the various caring professions - who may care very little for anyone except themselves, their salaries and state entitlements;
    iv.   philosophy signifies professors - who may know the technicalities of a subject but still lack insight and originality;
    v.   politics signifies parliamentarians - who may shout more often than they think;
    vi.   faith signifies clergy - except that they may be merely dogmatic.

2. Each of these concepts needs to be reclaimed into the individual domain: a balanced and committed life, such as we would hope for in recovery, needs to acknowledge individual responsibility for our minds. We may have our own specific interests and skills but we cannot afford to delegate or abdicate in the world of ideas.

3. Central to the belief in individualism (as opposed to the corporatist belief that nanny - in various disguises - knows best) is a sense of faith in ourselves and our capacity to influence our own lives in any way we wish:

    i.   we may not always get what we want or think we need but we do have the capacity to make the best use of what we have got;
    ii.   the future may at times appear very gloomy but that is no reason to destroy today;
    iii. a particular event may shatter a specific previous hope but there is plenty of room in a healthy psyche for new hope even in that same area of life, let alone in others.

4. Blind faith is stupid and stubborn, putting our heads down and charging through other people's beliefs and the events of life without being prepared to be influenced. In active addiction we may have a religious "faith" and the determined "faith" that we know what is best for ourselves. In recovery, faith can be open and trusting, knowing that whatever happens can be interpreted as an opportunity to learn and that we can free ourselves from the prison of our own previous experience and current concepts. In recovery we are acutely aware that previously we made a profound mess of running our own lives in our own way. Now we have to open our minds to wider concepts than the virtue of willpower. Instead of being at war with ourselves and other people in our determined efforts to see and do things our own way, we develop a sense of peace - of faith - in accepting that we have a great deal to learn from any individual and from any event. Our perception switches from seeing the glass as half empty to seeing it as half full and having the capacity to be full to the brim if we stop giving ourselves a daily dose of negativity.

5. Faith is far more than mere optimism. It is a deep sense of gratitude, an absolute commitment to daily enthusiasm, and a profound sense of trust that life is for living and that we have the power to create our own future when we learn to get out of our own way. We have nothing to fear except our own arrogance.

Confusion

The state of mind that exists after use of a mood-altering substance, behaviour or relationship.

The intellectual defence of using addicts when confronted with rational argument.

The mental and emotional battle between addictive disease and the human being it affects.

The attempt to prove that black is white.

Rebellion or aggression without a cause.

The absence of clear values.

Spiritual theories in the absence of spiritual reality.

The pursuit of excess.

Going to extremes, maximising or minimising.

Forgetting which mask one is wearing.

Failure to differentiate humility from humiliation.

The belief that one is a victim.

The sensation of being trapped.

Fear of fear.

Hopelessness.

Serenity

Peace of mind.

Restfulness of spirit.

Consciousness.

Clarity.

The return of choice.

Not repeating old mistakes.

Freedom.

Balance.

Acceptance.

The ability to appreciate other people.

Tolerance.

Forgiveness.

Awareness of one's own shortcomings.

The consequence of asking for help.

Confidence.

Ease.

Grace.

Loyalty

Addictive disease is loyal to addictive disease:

1. Using addicts share the same macabre values that protect their addiction. They pour scorn on abstinence.

2. Using addicts defend their relationships with each other in order to escape self-loathing and the criticisms of other people.

3. Using addicts despise each other.

4. Using addicts know all about addiction.

5. Using addicts tell lies in order to protect each other. They attack recovering addicts in order to protect their own continuing addiction while rejecting the constructive opportunities of recovery.

6. Using addicts despair.

Recovery is loyal to recovery:

1. Recovering addicts share the same positive values that protect their recovery. They reject the values of addictive disease.

2. Recovering addicts defend their relationships with each other in order to enhance self-esteem and the appreciation of other people.

3. Recovering addicts respect each other.

4. Recovering addicts know something about recovery.

5. Recovering addicts tell the truth in order to support each other. They confront using addicts appropriately and sensitively with the reality of their addiction, encouraging them to reverse the progressive destruction of addiction and gain the peace of mind and creativity of recovery.

6. Recovering addicts have hope for the future.

Living in Today

The past is over:

1. I cannot go back and live it again.

2. The only purpose of reflecting on the past is to learn from it.

3. My childhood was important in shaping me then: it doesn't have to continue to shape me now.

4. My "inner child" can become an obsessive preoccupation that keeps me stuck in resentments over past events.

5. Whatever may have happened to me or whatever I may have done in the past, I can learn now to forgive and love.

6. My past relationships live inside my head. I can choose to heal the past by healing my side of any relationship, even when the other person is absent or dead.

The future is yet to come:

1. I cannot live it in advance.

2. The only purpose of projecting into the future is to make sensible plans.

3. My present shapes my future; my hopes or fears for the future are not inevitable, they can be shaped into reality according to my wishes and in response to my own thoughts, feelings, actions and reactions.

4. My "inner child" can be a reminder to have some fun in the present and future.

5. Whatever may happen in the future, I can learn to treasure each day and the old relationships I renew or the new relationship I create within it.

6. My present and future relationships live inside my head. I can choose to create them in any way I wish by focusing upon my own attitudes and behaviour.

Anonymity

1. Tradition XII of the Anonymous Fellowships states "Anonymity is the spiritual foundation of all our Traditions, ever reminding us to place principles before personalities". Commonly in meetings of the Anonymous Fellowships there is a display card which states "Who you see here, what you hear here, when you leave here let it stay here". The principle of anonymity is central to the philosophy of the Twelve Step programme and vital to the survival of the Anonymous Fellowships.

2. Far from being secret societies, there are open meetings of the Anonymous Fellowships that anyone is welcome to attend. The ideas are widely published. In fact, since the very beginning of Alcoholics Anonymous, the members of the Anonymous Fellowships are very much concerned that the Twelve Step programme should be better known by the general public and perhaps particularly by the medical profession.

3. The individual members of the Anonymous Fellowships, and the stories they tell of their own experience, deserve anonymity. Many public figures are members of the Anonymous Fellowships but they are not there as public figures, only as themselves. Those members who have no public profile whatever may nonetheless fear exposure in one way or another.

4. The fear of public shame or ridicule is based not only upon the common belief in the general population that addictive behaviour is a disgrace and a product of weak will

and inadequate personality, but also upon addicts themselves initially sharing these beliefs. New members will not come forward to tackle their shame, make amends for their previous behaviour, and move on into a new life if the consequence of their honesty is for their personal stories to be blazoned abroad, sometimes with dire consequences to their employment or family life.

5.   Honesty, not simply cheque book honesty and George Washington honesty but honesty with ourselves in acknowledging our feelings, our behaviour and our difficulties, is essential if we are to remain in recovery from our addictive disease. Anything that jeopardises that process risks destroying us. We need to be honest with ourselves and to allow others to be honest with themselves so as to help us all to acknowledge our addictive disease and to combat our denial by seeing ourselves reflected in the group.

6.   Individual members of the Anonymous Fellowships may sometimes choose to break their anonymity (never that of other members) in order to counter the public perception of addictive disease as a disgrace and a one-way street downwards.

7.   The essential mood-altering process of the Anonymous Fellowships is that we ourselves feel better (and therefore have no need to change our feelings through the use of mood-altering substances, processes and relationships) when we reach out to help another sufferer. We see our own illness in his or hers. We offer hope without any thought of thanks for ourselves. If our identity is known we ourselves may get carried away with our own importance and other people may treat us as gurus. This benefits nobody. Furthermore, if professional medical or other therapeutic approaches to the treatment of addictive disease could have worked they would have done so but they didn't, whereas the Anonymous Fellowships do.

8.   The essential spiritual basis of anonymity is the community of all sufferers from addictive disease. We have no shortage of friends or interests in the outside world but in meetings of the Anonymous Fellowships we are simply ourselves, without any of our worldly trappings, alongside others of our own kind. If we lose that central awareness then our disease reasserts itself, with all its grandiosity and claims that we are special and different - and then we lose everything.

Fellowship Etiquette

1.   Our lives depend upon the integrity of the Anonymous Fellowships. Shipwrecked mariners would be well-advised not to damage the bottom of their lifeboats. Life-saving vessels need to be protected and well-maintained.

2.   The newcomer is the most important member of any group because he or she reminds us of where we come from and this protects us from becoming as arrogant in the Fellowships (because we think we know all the answers) as we were in the full flow of our active addiction.

3. It is only by reaching out to help newcomers that we ourselves gain continuing help by taking our minds off our own woes, resentments and demands.

4. There is an occasional curious belief that being honest about our feelings in a Fellowship meeting involves dumping a catalogue of disasters, complaints and negativity on to our hapless fellow members. Forcing them to listen to a tirade of self-pity and blame, and taking other people's inventories rather than our own, would be more likely to drive away newcomers - and everybody else - than attract them to stay. Of course it is appropriate to share our bad experiences as well as the good, our fears as well as our hopes, but there is absolutely nothing cleansing for ourselves or for anyone else if we merely pour a load of sludge into the meeting.

5. The Anonymous Fellowships exist in order that sufferers from addictive disease can get into remission by working the Twelve Step programme and sharing their experience, strength and hope. The Fellowships are not a forum for broadcasting a particular personal viewpoint. Concentrating on propagating our own idiosyncratic beliefs is what we did before: we come to the Fellowships to learn and to practise a new way of thinking, feeling and behaving.

6. On very rare occasions there are people who appear to cause deliberate damage to meetings. This is utterly bizarre but that seems to be the way it is. Perhaps their self-hatred becomes externalised. When this happens, the group needs to find appropriate ways - through a "Group Conscience" (administrative discussion) meeting to protect itself. Addictive disease is cunning, baffling and powerful: Anonymous Fellowships are fragile and they need to be nurtured.

7. Fellowship meetings are not run by a hierarchy: members take their turn in giving their time and talents to serve the well-being of individual groups and the Fellowships themselves. Without these willing contributions the Fellowships would die and, hence, so would we. It is up to each one of us to give to the Fellowships. Our experience is that we receive from the Fellowships in direct proportion to what we give to them.

8. The rooms in which Fellowship meetings are held have physical needs. If all we do is to help to keep them tidy - and absolutely anyone can make that contribution - then we shall have done something to support the meeting and the Fellowship.

9. Respecting anonymity means imagining that we have never met any member in the outside world and know nothing about them except what they share specifically in meetings.

10. The simple etiquette of thanking the speakers and other contributors to the meeting, keeping our own contributions short and to the point, and being courteous to, rather than critical of, our fellow members is an excellent reminder for subsequent appropriate behaviour in the outside world.

Suggestions to a Sponsee

We are not stupid. We have an illness - addictive disease - that is a disorder of mood and of perception: this illness "tells" us that we haven't got it. That is what is so frightening and so destructive. We are afflicted with an internal parasite of the human spirit that progressively destroys hope, trust, love, honour, innocence and the other characteristics that give life its beauty. Our illness wants us to itself : isolated and ultimately dead by our own hands, directly or indirectly. We need to recognise certain things and do certain things if we are to keep our illness at bay - one day at a time - so that we can have a happy and creative life.

1. If our way of controlling our feelings and our compulsive behaviour could have worked it would have done so. We have plenty of evidence from other aspects of our lives that we have an abundance of ability and determination. We have fine qualities but they do not work in treating addictive disease, any more than they would work for diabetes. This is simply an observable fact, when we take a good look at our lives. Our failure to control addictive or compulsive behaviour is not a disgrace nor a personal inadequacy.

2. We need to give up trying to do things our own way, doing the things that "should" work. We need to find a new way so that we can get better from this illness.

3. We need to give up all our addictive substances and processes right at the start, despite some people warning us that we should not do so. That is simply "disease talk": the illness doesn't like to be deprived of any of its nourishment. There is no point in hanging on to any addictive tendency: it will simply grow more powerful. Get rid of all addictions now. (Detoxification regimes require informed medical guidance.) Go through the withdrawals with the support of others and look forward to a real life with real feelings, not a poor imitation, dependent upon artificial stimuli in order to function at all.

4. At the start go to ninety Anonymous Fellowship meetings in ninety days, establishing a new sense of priority in life. We need to say something - anything - in every meeting, even if it is only our name and an acknowledgment of our addiction. This helps us to get involved in the meeting and subsequently get more out of it.

5. Stick with the winners, those who have something positive to contribute to meetings and whose personal lives and relationships show practical evidence of continuing recovery. Beware of gurus and one-to-one therapists: obsession with self is a feature of the illness, not of recovery.

6. Right from the start establish the routines of working Steps X, XI and XII each and every day:

   X. Get into the habit of taking our own inventory rather than other people's, writing down the good things as well as the bad;

XI. a) Whatever our troubles, get down on our knees (don't debate it, just do it: understanding comes later) and be grateful for what we have. Pray for courage, hope and persistence in the morning and express gratitude in the evening. Initially, pray for a maximum of one minute: that way there is no possible excuse for not doing it. The routine becomes established and that's what matters: getting out of our own way and gradually becoming aware of something greater than self. Start with a concept of prayer as merely a reminder to ourselves of our values in life. Start with a concept of God as Good Orderly Direction: the opposite of what we had before, when we were trying to do everything our own way;

b) Read something from the Anonymous Fellowship literature every day and ponder it for a few quiet moments;

XII. a) Reach out to help others, particularly when we most want help for ourselves. We keep only what we give away;

b) Apply the principles of Honesty, Open-mindedness, and Willingness (the HOW of recovery) in everything we do each day. It's tough - but the alternative is worse: we know that from our own experience.

7. Do something simply for pleasure each and every day. Recovery is a lot more than mere abstinence. Life is for living: it has to have purpose and it has to be fun.

The PROMIS Prayer

Help me, O God,
to be innocent and ignorant instead of all-knowing,
to be observant instead of arrogant,
to be questioning instead of certain,
to be able to be influenced instead of ever eager to influence others,
to be at peace with myself and others instead of ever critical.
O God give me the simplicity of spirit to be still.

Dr Robert Lefever 1988

The PROMIS Promise

I promise

to be fair and generous in spirit to myself and others,
to confront with kindness and understanding,
to be loyal to recovery, not to addictive disease.

The PROMIS Meditation

Be still and know that I am God
the crucible of creativity and the cradle of caring,
the home of happiness and the haven of hope,
the love of life and the life of love,
the glow of gratitude and the gentleness of grace,
the softness of simplicity and the serenity of silence.
Be still ... and *know* that I am God.

This meditation can be used as a contemplative journey into one's inner self if it is read with four beats to the line, breathing in on the first and third beats and out on the second and fourth as follows:

In		Out		In		Out
Be	still	and	know	that	I	am	God
the	crucible	of	creativity	and	the cradle	of	caring,
the	home	of	happiness	and	the haven	of	hope,
the	love	of	life	and	the life	of	love,
the	glow	of	gratitude	and	the gentleness	of	grace,
the	softness	of	simplicity	and	the serenity	of	silence.
Be	still	and	know	that	I	am	God

For each of us our concept of God will work for us when we feel that it is conscious and specifically relevant in our lives. Spiritual growth may be attainable through religious belief but the world's wars are often fought on sectarian divisions, and a modern scientific education does not look kindly upon mysticism, so some of us may choose to formulate our own spiritual belief in a non-religious Deity or Higher Power than self.

The PROMIS Reminders

1. My truth may be wrong: my head sometimes tells me lies.
2. Doing things exclusively my own way caused a lot of pain to other people and to myself.
3. My feelings are determined by whether my behaviour matches my true values.
4. I am responsible for my actions and reactions. Therefore I am responsible for my feelings.
5. Reaching out to help others counters the self-pity and blame of addictive disease.
6. Going to Anonymous Fellowship meetings counters denial: I see myself reflected in the mirror of the group.
7. Working (not merely reciting) the Twelve Steps counters anxiety and depression.
8. I do everything I am able to do. Then I can afford to relax: God looks after eventual outcomes.

Psychotherapeutic Approaches

	Perceived Defect		Treatment
1.	Permanent genetic impairment in neuro-transmission systems. Concept A. Addictive Disease. or B. Depressive illness.	A.	Abstinence from all mood-altering substances and processes PLUS working the XII Step programme on a continuing basis. Pharmaceutical drugs on a continuing basis.
		or B.	Continued attendance at Anonymous Fellowship Meetings.
2.	Permanent genetic impairment in perception. (Denial)		
3.	Long-standing imprint from childhood or other traumatic experience accessible to rational approach.	A.	Psychodynamic approaches including Cognitive Analytical Therapy. Cognitive Behavioural Therapy. Transactional Analysis. Gestalt. Choice Theory. Rogerian Person Centred Counselling. Rational Emotive Behaviour Therapy.
		or B.	E.M.D.R. Psychodrama.
4.	Long-standing imprint from childhood or other traumatic experience inaccessible to rational approach (locked in to "right" brain)		
5.	Transient perception deficits (misunderstandings and confusions).		Cognitive Behavioural Therapy. Rational Emotive Behaviour Therapy. Rogerian Person Centred Counselling. Neuro-Linguistic Programming. Choice Theory. Transactional Analysis. Gestalt.
6.	Transient emotional problem.	A.	Choice Theory. Transactional Analysis. Gestalt.
		or B.	E.M.D.R. Psychodrama.
		or C.	Pharmaceutical drugs to suppress symptoms.

Considerations on choice of therapeutic approach.

i.   Effectiveness.   Is the patient more functional as a result or is he or she a brainwashed zombie?
ii. Side-effects.   Is the patient fully functional mentally, emotionally and socially as a result of treatment?
                       Note: emotional health can only be achieved through acceptance of vulnerability.
iii. Time scale.   How long does treatment take to produce positive results?
iv. Financial cost.   What is the total financial cost of treatment and hence its accessibility to the general population?

a new life healing depression

171

Other books in the series

Preventing Addiction

Cigarette Smoking. Fifteen reasons for continuing to smoke (or not)

Healing

Dangerous Doctors

Common Sense in the Treatment of Eating Disorders

Spiritual Awakening. Working the Twelve Step programme

Inside the Madness

How to Combat Alcoholism and Addiction

How to Combat Anorexia, Bulimia and Compulsive Overeating

Spirituality for Atheists and Agnostics

Healthy Relationships

Prescription Drug Addiction. My doctor gave it to me

Behavioural Addictions: Workaholism. Shopaholism. Exercise Addiction. Gambling and Risk Taking. Self-Harming. Obsessive Compulsive Disorder

False Medical Gods

Detoxification and Harm Minimisation

Childhood Abuse and Abandonment

Healing Emotional Trauma with E.M.D.R.

Healing Emotional Trauma with Psychodrama

Treating Chronic Relapse. Not again

Help: The Dairy of a Private Doctor

    Vol 1: I will *not* make do. The philosophy and politics of help

    Vol 2: Daughters are Difficult. Professional help in clinical practice

    Vol 3: Henry is a Good Man. The boundaries of help

    Vol 4: Robin's turn. Beyond help